Lingering Pathogenic Illness

fú xié 伏邪

An Herbal Handbook

By Dr. Michael Moran, D.Ac., L.Ac.

New Orleans, Louisiana

Copyright

For inquiries, permissions, or professional contact, please email:
michael@acunola.com

ISBN (Paperback): 979-8-89122-632-6
ISBN (Hardcover): 979-8-89122-633-3

Dedication

To all those living with complex, misunderstood illnesses:
Your courage is unmatched, and your suffering deserves not just relief but recognition.

To my patients, past and present, whose stories have shaped this work, and to all who seek to understand: may this be a light in the dark.

"Illnesses that do not resolve must be treated as though the evils still remain within."
- Zhang Zhongjing, *Jin Gui Yao Lue*

Acknowledgments

I am deeply grateful to the many physicians, scholars, and healers who have laid the foundation for our understanding of Lingering Pathogenic Illness, Gu Syndrome, and lurking or lingering heat toxins. Their insights, observations, and clinical mastery have shaped the way we understand chronic and hidden illness in Chinese medicine.

This list is by no means exhaustive, but it honors some of the most influential voices across the centuries:

Zhang Zhongjing (150–219 CE), Ge Hong (283–343 CE), Tao Hongjing (456–536 CE), Sun Simiao (581–682 CE), Chen Wuze (d. ~1170 CE), Liu Wansu (1110–1200 CE), Zhang Congzheng (1156–1228 CE), Wu Youke (1582–1652), Ye Tianshi (1666–1745 CE), Yang Lishan (1705–?), Wu Jutong (1758–1836), Jiang Baosu (1794–1893), Liu Bao-Yi (1842–1901), Zhou Xuehai (1856–1906), and many others.

I offer this work in continuity with theirs, with humility and reverence.

I am also indebted to those who helped shape this book in the present day: Liliana, Clarissa, Doug, Heiner, and Arnaud, who offered me their support. Finally, I owe profound thanks to the ME community, whose disability doula-ship toward those of us newly disabled offered hard-won wisdom, solidarity, and care, which made much of this work possible.

This book is for educational purposes only and is not intended to diagnose, treat, or replace personalized medical care. Always consult a licensed healthcare provider for health-related concerns.

Table Of Contents

Preface

I did not set out to write a book about Lingering Pathogenic Illness[1], complex chronic illnesses marked by immune dysfunction that do not resolve. I was led to this endeavor by necessity, by my and my patients' desperation for relief, by the wisdom that kept surfacing in the classical texts when I went looking for answers, and by the urgent need to bridge this information from ancient physicians to modern patients.

This journey is not just professional. I am also a patient. I live with Myalgic Encephalomyelitis (ME)[2], and Long Covid,[3] overlapping conditions. I have spent years inside the labyrinth of misdiagnosis, gaslighting, improper treatment, and outright indifference that defines life with a complex chronic illness. I have been told to change my perspective. I have been referred to physical therapy more than any other specialty (to my detriment). I have been told to drink sugary corn syrup drinks to gain weight. This book is written not just with clinical training, but with the all-too-common experience of having tried what seems like everything, including things that definitely do not work, to feel better.

I am also an activist and independent researcher. I believe that, though our medical systems are more than equipped to care for patients, they simply choose not to. The framework of Chinese medicine, particularly its treatment of lingering pathogens, Gu syndrome[4], and unresolved febrile disease, offers a language and a logic that can restore coherence to what has been fragmented by modern medical paradigms.

---

[1] Lingering Pathogenic Illness: A condition in which remnants of an unresolved pathogen - such as viral debris or immune-metabolic signals - persist after acute illness or injury, leading to chronic symptoms like fatigue, brain fog, and immune dysregulation. This pattern underlies syndromes like Long Covid, ME/CFS, and chronic Lyme, and calls for phased treatment that alternates between expelling lingering pathogens and restoring Zheng Qi(Upright Qi).

[2] Myalgic Encephalomyelitis (ME/CFS): A chronic, multi-system illness characterized by post-exertional malaise, unrefreshing sleep, cognitive dysfunction, and profound fatigue. It often follows viral infection and involves mitochondrial dysfunction, immune dysregulation, and impaired energy metabolism. Closely associated with Long Covid in both pathophysiology and clinical presentation.

[3] Long Covid: A post-acute sequela of SARS-CoV-2 infection characterized by prolonged, multi-system symptoms including fatigue (often with post-exertional malaise), brain fog, dysautonomia, and chronic inflammation. It shares clinical features with ME/CFS, mast cell activation syndrome, and post-treatment Lyme disease. Emerging models suggest that immune complex persistence, antigen-presenting cell dysfunction, and loss of immune tolerance are key immunopathological drivers.

[4] Gu Toxin (Gu Syndrome): A classical Chinese medicine concept describing complex, chronic, often parasitic or toxin-driven illness with psychological, digestive, and systemic symptoms. Originally associated with tropical

In the *Jin Gui Yao Lue*[5], Zhang Zhongjing[6] warns us that, "illnesses that do not resolve must be treated as though the evils still remain within."[7] This statement is not just diagnostic; it is compassionate. And it is the foundation of this work.

What follows is neither comprehensive nor final. It is what I know right now, rooted in practice, shaped by lineage, lived in the body, and offered with humility.

This is a handbook, meant to be used, argued with, and referenced in moments of uncertainty. It's written for a wide audience: for clinicians frustrated by the limits of conventional tools; for practitioners of East Asian medicine seeking to ground ancient theory in modern pathology; for researchers and thinkers exploring chronic illness at the edge of biomedical consensus; and for patients, especially those who have not been believed, who seek language that validates their experience. It is for anyone who senses that the path forward requires drawing from both science and history, where evolving knowledge meets enduring wisdom.

- Michael Moran, D.Ac., L.Ac.
New Orleans, Louisiana 2025

---

disease and food poisoning, Gu now serves as a metaphor for difficult-to-treat, multi-system chronic illness involving lingering pathogens, dysbiosis, and immune disruption—such as in Long Covid and ME/CFS.

[5] *Jin Gui Yao Lue*: Translated as *Essential Prescriptions of the Golden Cabinet*, this classical text by Zhang Zhongjing focuses on the diagnosis and treatment of complex internal disorders. A companion to the *Shang Han Lun*, it emphasizes chronic illness, deficiency patterns, gynecology, and organ-based pathology, offering many foundational formulas still used in clinical practice today.

[6] Zhang Zhongjing: A foundational physician of the Eastern Han dynasty (c. 150–219 CE) and originator of the Cold Damage (Shang Han) school. He authored the *Shang Han Lun* and *Jin Gui Yao Lue*, establishing the six-stage model of disease progression and many formulas still central to Chinese medicine. His work laid the foundation for treating externally contracted and internally generated illnesses through pattern differentiation.

[7] Text: *Jīn Guì Yào Lüè* (金匱要略)
Section: Miscellaneous Diseases (雜病篇), Discussion of Latent Heat and Recurrence
Attributed Author: Zhang Zhongjing (張仲景)
Original (related principle): "病久不愈，必有餘邪。"
Translation: "When illness does not resolve for a long time, there must be residual pathogenic Qi."

Introduction: Lingering Pathogenic Illness

First, let's review some foundational concepts of Lingering Pathogenic Illness before we dive into the deeper historical and clinical context. Don't forget to check the footnotes and glossary if you need clarification, whether on Chinese medicine or broader biomedical terminology.

Not all illnesses resolve.

Some appear to pass, fevers break, rashes fade, test results normalize, only for new, stranger symptoms to emerge in their wake: fatigue that becomes disabling; a mind that grows foggy; an immune system that begins to react to everything, or seemingly nothing. These patients live in a chronic state: no longer acutely ill, but very far from well. This is the territory of Lingering Pathogenic Illness (LPI).

In classical Chinese medicine, this state of enduring illness has long been recognized. In some cases, pathogens that fail to be fully expelled may retreat deeper into the body, lodging in membranes and energetic systems, where they quietly disturb function over time. These are the "residual evils," described as early as the *Su Wen*[8], reemerging in later dynasties as "lodged heat,"[9] "membrane source pathogens,"[10] and "hidden toxins."[11] Though these pathogens may not always

---

[8] Text: *Huáng Dì Nèi Jīng Sù Wèn* (黃帝內經·素問)
Section: Chapter 58 - *Qì Jiāo Biàn Dà Lùn* (氣交變大論)
Attributed Author: Huáng Dì (黃帝, The Yellow Emperor)
Original: "邪之所湊，其氣必虛。"
Translation: "Wherever pathogenic Qi gathers, the Qi must be deficient."

[9] Text: *Wēn Bìng Lùn* (溫病論)
Section: Initial Discussion of Spring Warmth (春溫初起)
Attributed Author: Ye Tianshi (葉天士, 1666–1745)
Original: "身熱不惡寒者，熱伏於裏也。"
Translation: "When the body is hot without aversion to cold, the Heat is lodged in the interior."

[10] Text: *Wēn Rè Lùn* (溫熱論)
Section: Discussion of Warm Heat Entering the Membrane Source (溫熱犯膜原)
Attributed Author: Ye Tianshi (葉天士, 1666–1745)
Original: "邪伏膜原，不即傳經。"
Translation: "The pathogen is trapped in the Membrane Source and does not immediately transmit to the channels."

[11] Text: *Wēn Yì Lùn* (瘟疫論)

provoke overt fever or pain, their presence disrupts the body's ability to regulate and repair itself.

In modern biomedical terms, Lingering Pathogenic Illness can be viewed as corresponding to aspects of chronic, post-infectious, and immune-mediated syndromes. These may include, but are not limited to:

- Chronic and post-viral infections: Epstein-Barr virus[12], cytomegalovirus[13], post-influenza syndromes, Long Covid, Long Ebola[14], etc.
- Myalgic Encephalomyelitis (ME/CFS).

Section: Preface and General Discussion of Pestilential Qi (瘟疫總論)
Attributed Author: Wu Youke (吳又可, 1582–1652)
Original: "毒氣伏於內，久而不發，遇虛則發。"
Translation: "Toxic Qi may hide internally and not erupt for a long time; when weakness arises, it emerges."

[12] Epstein-Barr Virus (EBV): A ubiquitous herpesvirus that establishes lifelong latency in B cells after initial infection, which is often asymptomatic or presents as mononucleosis. In the context of Long Covid and ME/CFS, EBV is clinically significant due to its potential for viral reactivation under conditions of immune stress or dysregulation. Reactivated EBV may contribute to chronic inflammation, fatigue, neurocognitive symptoms, and immune exhaustion, particularly through its effects on B cells, antigen-presenting cells, and cytokine signaling. Emerging evidence suggests that EBV reactivation may serve as a cofactor or amplifier in post-viral syndromes by compounding immune dysfunction and promoting viral persistence dynamics similar to those seen in Long Covid.

[13] Cytomegalovirus (CMV): A beta-herpesvirus that establishes lifelong latency following primary infection, often asymptomatic in healthy individuals but capable of reactivation under immune stress. In the context of Long Covid and ME/CFS, CMV is significant for its ability to reshape the immune landscape, particularly through expansion of terminally differentiated T cells and chronic activation of innate immune pathways. Reactivation of CMV has been associated with inflammatory imprinting, immune exhaustion, and impaired antiviral responses, potentially contributing to persistent fatigue, cognitive dysfunction, and poor recovery in post-viral syndromes. Like EBV, CMV may act as a latent cofactor, aggravating immune dysregulation and interfering with resolution of primary infections such as SARS-CoV-2.

[14] Long Ebola: A post-acute sequela of Ebola virus disease (EVD) characterized by persistent symptoms and delayed complications after apparent recovery. Its pathomechanism is thought to involve dendritic cell (DC) dysfunction during acute infection, which impairs antigen presentation and immune resolution. This allows Ebola virus to persist in immune-privileged sites such as the eyes, central nervous system, and testes, where it may form latent or low-replication reservoirs. These reservoirs contribute to chronic inflammation, neurologic and ocular complications, and even viral recrudescence. Long Ebola offers a model for understanding other post-viral syndromes involving viral persistence and immune dysregulation, including Long Covid and ME/CFS.

- ❖ Chronic bacterial and fungal infections: Lyme disease[15], candida[16], toxoplasmosis[17], etc.
- ❖ Allergies, food intolerances, mold[18], and environmental Illnesses.
- ❖ Post-vaccination syndromes[19], post-chemotherapy syndromes[20], post-traumatic disorders.

---

[15] Lyme Disease (Long Lyme, Chronic Lyme): An illness caused by infection with *Borrelia burgdorferi*, typically transmitted by ticks. While most acute cases resolve with antibiotics, a subset of patients experience long-term symptoms - termed Long Lyme or Chronic Lyme - including fatigue, cognitive changes, joint pain, and neurological dysfunction. Like Long Covid, it may involve persistent antigens, immune dysregulation, and disrupted homeostasis.

[16] Candida: A genus of yeast-like fungi that commonly inhabit the human microbiome, particularly in the gastrointestinal and genitourinary tracts. While typically commensal, Candida can become opportunistically pathogenic when mucosal immunity is impaired or microbial balance is disrupted. In the context of Long Covid and ME/CFS, Candida overgrowth may emerge due to immune dysregulation, reduced secretory IgA, antibiotic use, or gut barrier dysfunction, contributing to symptoms such as bloating, brain fog, food intolerances, and fatigue. Chronic Candida may amplify innate immune activation and Th17-skewed responses, potentially reinforcing inflammatory loops already present in post-viral syndromes. Though not a root cause, Candida is considered a secondary burden that can exacerbate symptom persistence and metabolic stress in vulnerable patients.

[17] Toxoplasmosis: An infection caused by the protozoan parasite *Toxoplasma gondii*, which establishes chronic, often asymptomatic latency in host tissues—especially in the brain, eyes, and muscle. In immunocompetent individuals, the infection is typically controlled but not eradicated. In the context of Long Covid and ME/CFS, toxoplasmosis is significant for its potential to modulate neuroimmune signaling, impair microglial regulation, and alter dopamine and glutamate pathways. Latent *T. gondii* may reactivate or exert low-grade neuroinflammatory effects under conditions of immune dysregulation, possibly contributing to fatigue, mood disturbance, and cognitive dysfunction. While not considered a primary driver, it is viewed as a potential cofactor in post-viral illness, particularly in cases marked by persistent neuroinflammation or immune surveillance deficits.

[18] Mold: Various species of fungi that can grow indoors or in damp environments, producing spores and, in some cases, mycotoxins that affect human health. In the context of Long Covid and ME/CFS, mold exposure is significant as a non-infectious but immunologically active environmental trigger. For sensitive individuals—particularly those with impaired detoxification pathways, HLA-DR susceptibility, or prior immune compromise—mold exposure can provoke chronic inflammatory responses, mast cell activation, and neuroimmune dysregulation. Symptoms often mimic or compound post-viral syndromes, including fatigue, cognitive dysfunction, temperature instability, and post-exertional malaise. Mold is considered a perpetuating factor in recovery from viral illness, and unrecognized mold exposure may inhibit healing or lead to misattribution of symptoms to lingering infection alone.

[19] Post-Vaccination Syndromes: Persistent symptom complexes that develop following immunization with either mRNA-based or traditional (e.g., viral vector, protein subunit, or inactivated) vaccines. Reported symptoms may include chronic fatigue, cognitive dysfunction, autonomic instability, myalgias, and immune dysregulation, often resembling syndromes such as Long Covid or ME/CFS. Proposed mechanisms include innate immune hyperactivation, mast cell involvement, molecular mimicry, and dysregulation of Fc gamma receptor (FcγR) signaling, particularly in individuals with genetic or acquired immune sensitivity. In the case of viral or mRNA-based vaccines encoding spike proteins, some hypotheses suggest that persistent spike protein expression or circulation—in combination with impaired antigen-presenting cell (APC) clearance - may contribute to ongoing immune stimulation in a subset of patients. Post-vaccination syndromes merit thoughtful clinical investigation and research attention, especially given their shared immunological features with post-viral illness.

[20] Post-Chemotherapy Syndromes: A cluster of persistent physical, cognitive, and psychological symptoms that occur after the completion of cancer treatment—often lasting months or years beyond remission. These may include fatigue, brain fog, neuropathy, immune suppression, dysautonomia, and mood disturbances. Mechanistically, post-chemotherapy syndromes are thought to result from mitochondrial damage, chronic inflammation, and lasting

❖ Autoimmune and inflammatory diseases: systemic lupus erythematosus[21], rheumatoid arthritis, Hashimoto's[22], etc.[23]

What ties these conditions together is not their surface presentation, but a similar immune phenomenon: a failure of resolution and a loss of tolerance.

Recent research provides insight into what may underlie this pattern. For the purposes of this book, I focus on one recurring theme in the literature: the possible dysfunction of antigen-presenting cells (APCs),[24] including dendritic cells, B cells, and monocytes.[25][26] These cells are responsible not only for initiating immune

---

alterations to immune surveillance, including dysfunction of dendritic cells and antigen-presenting pathways. Chemotherapeutic agents may also disrupt the gut microbiome and blood–brain barrier, compounding neuroimmune injury. In the context of Long Covid and ME/CFS, these syndromes are increasingly recognized as parallel expressions of acquired chronic illness, marked by overlapping features such as post-exertional malaise, autonomic dysfunction, and impaired recovery from stressors.

[21] Systemic Lupus Erythematosus (SLE): A chronic, multisystem autoimmune disease characterized by the production of autoantibodies and immune complex deposition that leads to widespread inflammation and tissue damage. A central feature of SLE pathophysiology is Fc gamma receptor (FcγR) dysfunction, which contributes to defective clearance of immune complexes and aberrant activation of innate immune cells such as dendritic cells, macrophages, and neutrophils. Dysregulated FcγR signaling amplifies type I interferon responses and promotes a self-sustaining loop of autoimmunity, particularly affecting the skin, kidneys, joints, and central nervous system. In the context of Long Covid and ME/CFS, SLE serves as a model for chronic immune activation, antigen presentation abnormalities, and loss of tolerance, offering insight into post-viral autoimmunity and Fc receptor-mediated pathology.

[22] Hashimoto's Thyroiditis: An autoimmune disorder in which the immune system targets and gradually destroys the thyroid gland, most commonly leading to hypothyroidism. It is characterized by the presence of anti-thyroid peroxidase (TPO) and anti-thyroglobulin antibodies, along with lymphocytic infiltration of thyroid tissue. Hashimoto's involves impaired antigen-presenting cell (APC) regulation and loss of self-tolerance, often in the setting of Fc gamma receptor (FcγR) dysfunction and heightened type I interferon signaling. In the context of Long Covid and ME/CFS, Hashimoto's is notable both for its shared patterns of immune dysregulation and for its prevalence as a comorbidity. Fluctuating thyroid hormone levels may exacerbate fatigue, cognitive dysfunction, and thermoregulatory issues, making screening essential in patients with post-viral or chronic inflammatory syndromes.

[23] Lyttleton, Jane, and William Maclean. *Clinical Handbook of Internal Medicine: The Treatment of Disease with Traditional Chinese Medicine, Vol. 3: Qi, Blood, Fluid and Channel Disorders*. Seattle: Eastland Press, 2019.

[24] Antigen-presenting Cell(APC): A type of immune cell—such as a dendritic cell, macrophage, or B cell - that processes and presents antigens to T cells, initiating and regulating immune responses. In chronic illness, APC dysfunction can impair both immune activation and tolerance, contributing to persistent inflammation and autoimmunity.

[25] Zao, Ruxing. "Immunometabolic Changes and Potential Biomarkers in CFS Peripheral Immune Cells Revealed by Single-Cell RNA Sequencing." Journal of Translational Medicine, vol. 22, no. 10, 2024, article 285, https://doi.org/10.1186/s12967-024-05710-w

[26] Guerrera, Giorgia, et al. "Identification of an Immunological Signature of Long COVID Syndrome." *Frontiers in Immunology*, vol. 15, 2025, article 1502937, https://doi.org/10.3389/fimmu.2024.1502937

responses, but also for deciding when *not* to react. When APCs are driven past their prime, by viral persistence, immune complexes[27], metabolic stress, or repeated activation, they lose both antigenic and tolerogenic tone. The result is a system unable to clear what does not belong and incapable of tolerating what does. This model of APC dysfunction and immune hyperreactivity mirrors the Chinese medicine understanding of Qi deficiency[28], Yin damage[29], and pathogenic heat trapped in the deeper levels of the body seen in Lingering Pathogenic Illnesses.

This book is written as a bridge between two systems: immunology and classical Chinese medicine. It suggests that Lingering Pathogenic Illness need not be viewed as a "mystery diagnosis," but rather as a possible outcome of failed immune resolution. Each chapter offers a framework that draws from classical Chinese pathophysiology and modern immunology, supported by case studies and clinical strategies. At the end, I offer an additional custom base formula designed to mobilize trapped pathogens, restore immune function, and gradually support recovery.

This book is for practitioners ready to rethink chronic illness, for patients who have not been believed, and for those of us thinking forward, without reinventing the wheel, drawing on ancient knowledge as much as modern science, in a space where medicine and the lived body still have room to evolve.

---

[27] Immune Complex: A cluster of antigens bound to antibodies (usually IgG). If not cleared effectively by phagocytes, these complexes can deposit in tissues and perpetuate inflammation - a key feature of autoimmunity and Lingering Pathogenic Illness.

[28] Qi Deficiency: A core diagnostic pattern involving fatigue, shortness of breath, poor digestion, and weak immunity. Qi is the animating force of all physiological function. Deficiency may result from overwork, illness, or chronic inflammation. Common in LPI, where immune and metabolic systems become underpowered and recovery is impaired.

[29] Yin Deficiency (Yin Damage): A pattern marked by depletion of the body's cooling and moistening functions, often after heat illness, overwork, or blood loss. Symptoms include night sweats, dry mouth, insomnia, and a red, peeled tongue. Also called "Yin damage," it can lead to empty heat and internal agitation, especially in later-stage or Shaoyin disorders.

Chapter One: A History of Lingering Pathogenic Illness

Now that we've established our bearings, let's take a chronological walk through the history of Chinese medicine, tracing how the theory of lingering pathogenic illness has evolved across the classical canon.

Although Lingering Pathogenic Illness is a relatively new term, the concept in Chinese medicine is as old as the medicine itself. From the Shang dynasty's use of oracle bones to contemporary herbal clinics treating Long Covid, the idea that disease may persist after its apparent resolution has remained a consistent, albeit often overlooked, theme in both classical literature and modern research.

Symbols for "Gu" worm spirits

Oracle Bone　Seal Script　Chinese Character

Ancient Chinese medicine was far more shamanic in tone than what we now call Traditional Chinese Medicine(standardized in the 20th century). Lingering pathogens were described as "Gu," malefic worm spirits that consumed the body from within. Gu was a kind of energetic rot, often associated with sorcery or ritual poisoning, used to curse enemies in the Shang dynasty. Gu wasn't just a metaphor, though; it reflected clinical realities, strange illnesses that defied explanation and eroded the body slowly from the inside out.

As Paul Unschuld[30] has noted, early Chinese medicine lived at the intersection of demonology, nature philosophy, and ritual healing.[31] A diagnosis like Gu wasn't just about microbes or toxins; it reflected a cosmological and moral disturbance. It meant something had gone deeply wrong in the human-environment-spirit interface. And even as later Chinese medicine evolved into a more systematic and internally consistent science, those older frameworks never entirely disappeared. What was once referred to in a more spiritual sense was simply given new names with biomedical corollaries.

The *Huang Di Nei Jing Su Wen*[32] describes how external evils can lodge deep in the body and remain hidden, reemerging later when the system weakens.[33] People recovered from fevers, only to relapse or deteriorate in subtler ways. The ancient doctors recognized that if symptoms lingered, so did the cause.

Zhang Zhongjing (150-219 CE), author of the *Shang Han Lun*[34] and *Jin Gui Yao Lue*, laid out protocols for this very scenario. His discussion of Shaoyang[35] disorders, conditions that hover between the interior and exterior, captures the stuckness of

---

[30] Paul Unschuld: A contemporary scholar and historian of Chinese medicine, best known for his translations and analyses of classical medical texts, including the *Huang Di Nei Jing* and *Nan Jing*. His work emphasizes the historical, philosophical, and political contexts of Chinese medical thought, often highlighting its differences from Western biomedical models. Unschuld's research has been influential in bringing critical academic attention to the conceptual foundations of Chinese medicine in the modern era.

[31] Paul U. Unschuld, *Medicine in China: A History of Ideas* (Berkeley: University of California Press, 1985), 33–41.

[32] *Huang Di Nei Jing Su Wen: The Su Wen* ("Basic Questions") is one half of the foundational text *Huang Di Nei Jing* ("Yellow Emperor's Inner Classic"), compiled around the 2nd century BCE. Presented as a dialogue between the Yellow Emperor and his ministers, it outlines core principles of Chinese medicine—Yin-Yang, the Five Phases, Qi dynamics, seasonal adaptation, and the causes of disease—forming the theoretical basis for diagnosis and treatment.

[33] *Huáng Dì Nèi Jīng Sù Wèn* (黃帝內經·素問), Chapter 3: *Shēng Qì Tōng Tiān Lùn* (生氣通天論).
"When pathogenic Qi lodges in the body: if it is deep, it remains; if shallow, it is released."
Original: "邪氣之客於身也，深者留之，淺者出之。"

[34] *Shang Han Lun*: Translated as *Treatise on Cold Damage*, this seminal text by Zhang Zhongjing outlines the diagnosis and treatment of externally contracted febrile diseases. Based on the six-stage model (Taiyang to Jueyin), it provides a systematic approach to disease progression and contains many core formulas used to treat both acute and chronic conditions.

[35] Shaoyang: One of the six divisions of channel theory, representing the pivot between interior and exterior. Dysregulation here leads to alternating symptoms (chills/fever, appetite swings), unresolved infection, and poor detoxification. Key in post-viral syndromes.

lingering illness. He wrote, "Illnesses that do not resolve must be treated as though the evils still remain within."[36]

Zhang Zhongjing also emphasized that lingering illness can be detected early: "Before disease erupts, the pulse may already reveal internal constraint."[37] And elsewhere, he cautions, "In Shaoyin[38] illness, at the beginning, there may be fever. If the pulse is deep, this indicates internal Heat. If, after treatment, the patient becomes restless and cannot lie down, with palpitations, it is pathogenic Heat in the interior; there will be diarrhea. Treat with *Huang Lian E Jiao Tang*."[39] Here, Zhang Zhongjing warns of lingering heat in the Shaoyin channel of the body if there is fever with a deep pulse, as opposed to a superficial pulse, which would likely indicate a more superficial pathogen.

He prescribes Gui Zhi Jia Huang Qi Tang for "taxation relapse,"[40] a pattern where illness lingers due to failure to rest. This formula, now understood to have immune-activating effects, is used to support the antigen-presenting function of the body and to push pathogens back outward. A Gui Zhi Jia Huang Qi Tang pulse is likely

---

[36] Text: *Jīn Guì Yào Lüè* (金匱要略)
Section: Miscellaneous Diseases (雜病篇), Discussion of Latent Heat and Recurrence
Attributed Author: Zhang Zhongjing (張仲景)
Original (related principle): "病久不愈，必有餘邪。"
Translation: "When illness does not resolve for a long time, there must be residual pathogenic Qi."

[37] Text: *Jīn Guì Yào Lüè* (金匱要略)
Section: Miscellaneous Diseases (雜病篇)
Attributed Author: Zhang Zhongjing (張仲景)
Original: "診脈證並治，欲解內鬱，當審其脈。"
Translation: "To resolve internal constraint, one must examine the pulse carefully."

[38] Shaoyin: The Yin-most of the six stages, involving the Heart and Kidney. Imbalances may lead to deficiency heat, Yang deficiency, or interior cold. Often implicated in fatigue, dysautonomia, and deep-level immune dysfunction.

[39] Text: *Shāng Hán Lùn* (傷寒論)
Section: Shaoyin Illness, Line 303
Formula: Huang Lian E Jiao Tang (黃連阿膠湯)
Attributed Author: Zhang Zhongjing (張仲景)
Original: "少陰病，得之二三日以上，心中煩，不得臥者，黃連阿膠湯主之。"
Translation: "In Shaoyin disease, if there is fever with a deep pulse, this indicates internal Heat - Huang Lian E Jiao Tang is appropriate. If the patient is restless and cannot lie down, Huang Lian E Jiao Tang governs."

[40] Taxation Relapse (Láo Fù): A relapse of disease symptoms triggered by physical or mental overexertion during a phase of apparent recovery. Originally described by Zhang Zhongjing in the *Shāng Hán Lùn*, taxation relapse reflects a failure to conserve and replenish vital Qi following illness or mistreatment.

“floating” or superficial and forceless due to an underlying deficiency, indicating a relatively recent onset that has failed to resolve despite sweating.[41]

Zhang Zhongjing also described patterns that cycle seasonally: “Some patients suffer a sudden bout of dysentery on the same days each year.”[42] His writings suggest that Lingering Pathogenic Illness can go unrecognized for long periods, sometimes a year or more, manifesting only in subtle signs like allergies, autoimmunity, or food intolerances until a larger flare erupts. I’ve seen this firsthand in my clinic: in the extreme heat and humidity of New Orleans, certain patients develop nearly identical bouts of digestive distress at the same time every year. At first, I mistook it for a purely deficient pattern, but in time, it revealed itself as lingering internal heat, aggravated by environmental conditions.

Ge Hong[43] (283-343 CE), in his *Zhou Hou Bei Ji Fang*[44], warned of pathogens that “do not leave the bones,” and wrote extensively about conditions that involved

---

[41]Text: *Jīn Guì Yào Lüè* (金匱要略), Chapter on Taxation Injury (勞傷篇).
Attributed Author: Zhang Zhongjing.
Original: “發汗後，身體腫，脈浮大者，桂枝加黃芪湯主之。”
Translation: “After sweating, if the body becomes swollen and the pulse is floating and large, Gui Zhi Jia Huang Qi Tang governs.”

[42] Text: *Jīn Guì Yào Lüè* (金匱要略)
Section: Dysenteric Disorders (痢病篇)
Attributed Author: Zhang Zhongjing (張仲景)
Original: “有患一年數度得噤病者，至其時則發；或一年一發，發必有時。”
Translation: “Some patients suffer repeated bouts of dysentery each year, occurring at the same time; or once yearly, but always at a fixed season.”

[43] Ge Hong: A physician, alchemist, and scholar of the Eastern Jin dynasty (283–343 CE), best known for his text *Zhou Hou Bei Ji Fang* (*Handbook of Prescriptions for Emergencies*). Ge Hong advanced early infectious disease treatment, promoted the use of minerals and potent herbs, and contributed to Daoist internal alchemy. His work reflects a blend of pragmatic clinical medicine and spiritual cultivation, influencing later developments in Chinese pharmacology and longevity practices.

[44] Zhou Hou Bei Ji Fang: Translated as *Handbook of Prescriptions for Emergencies*, a classic medical text compiled by Ge Hong during the Eastern Jin dynasty(~340 CE). The title literally means “Formulas to Keep at One’s Elbow for Emergencies,” reflecting its practical intent as a ready reference for urgent care. The work preserves over 1,000 prescriptions covering infectious diseases, epidemics, poisoning, wounds, and other acute conditions, often using readily available herbs and materials. It is notable for early references to variolation (smallpox inoculation), as well as practical instructions for preventing and treating epidemic disorders long before germ theory. Ge Hong’s emphasis on accessibility, adaptability, and speed of response influenced later public health approaches in Chinese medicine and established the text as one of the foundational handbooks of emergency and epidemic treatment.

wasting, madness, or the loss of one's vitality without clear cause.[45] Tao Hongjing[46] (456-536 CE), compiling and commenting on earlier materia medica, spoke of the toxic influence of Gu and its ability to transform over time, leading to corruption of both body and spirit.[47]

Sun Simiao[48] (581-682 CE) taught that a great physician must be able to recognize illness before it takes form, and wrote in the *Qian Jin Yao Fang*[49] of chronic

---

[45] Text: *Zhòu Hòu Bèi Jí Fāng* (肘後備急方)
Attributed Author: Ge Hong (葛洪)
Section: Cold Damage & Hidden Pathogens
Original: "邪留骨中不出。"
Translation: "The pathogen remains in the bones and does not come out."

[46] Tao Hongjing: A polymath of the Southern Dynasties period (456–536 CE), Tao Hongjing was a physician, alchemist, and scholar who compiled and annotated the *Shen Nong Ben Cao Jing Ji Zhu* (*Collected Commentaries on the Classic of the Materia Medica*). He systematized herbal knowledge, distinguished between authentic and counterfeit substances, and integrated Daoist cosmology with medical theory, laying the foundation for later developments in Chinese pharmacology and internal cultivation.

[47] Text: *Shén Nóng Běn Cǎo Jīng Jí Zhù* (神農本草經集注)
Section: Commentary on Toxic Substances and Gu (毒藥·蠱毒)
Attributed Author: Tao Hongjing (陶弘景, 456–536 CE)
Original: "蠱毒之變化無窮，久留則中人神氣。"
Translation: "The transformations of Gu toxin are endless; when retained long-term, it can strike both the body and the spirit."

[48] Sun Simiao: A renowned physician of the Sui and Tang dynasties (581–682 CE), often honored as the "King of Medicine." He is best known for his comprehensive texts *Qian Jin Yao Fang* (*Essential Prescriptions Worth a Thousand Gold*) and *Qian Jin Yi Fang* (*Supplement to the Thousand Gold Prescriptions*), which emphasize preventive care, ethical medical practice, and detailed clinical guidance. Sun integrated Daoist, Confucian, and Buddhist principles, elevating the moral and spiritual dimensions of medicine.

[49] Qian Jin Yao Fang: Translated as *Essential Prescriptions Worth a Thousand Gold Pieces*, a monumental Tang dynasty medical compendium written by Sun Simiao, often revered as the "King of Medicine." Completed around 652 CE, this work contains more than 5,300 prescriptions, organized into 30 volumes, covering internal medicine, gynecology, pediatrics, surgery, acupuncture, moxibustion, and dietetics. The title reflects Sun's conviction that life and health are worth more than a thousand pieces of gold. The text emphasizes preventive medicine, proper conduct of the physician, and the ethical duty to treat all patients equally, including women, children, and the poor - making it not only a clinical but also a moral landmark in Chinese medical history. Together with its companion volume, *Qian Jin Yi Fang* (Supplement to Prescriptions Worth a Thousand Gold Pieces), it laid a foundation for later medical practice and remains a key reference for classical formula study.

conditions that transform the temperament and damage the will.[50] Chen Wuze[51] (d. ~1170), whose *San Yin Ji Yi Bing Zheng Fang Lun*[52] emphasized hidden pathogenic factors, wrote that "when the evil does not show on the surface, the wise physician must seek it in the blood."[53]

Liu Wansu[54] (1110-1200), founder of the Cold and Cooling School, observed, "When fire is not extinguished, it hides and becomes the root of lingering disease."[55] His student Zhang Congzheng[56] emphasized expelling "stuck turbidities" that

---

[50] Text: *Qiān Jīn Yào Fāng* (千金要方)
Section: Volume 1 — On the Art of Medicine (大醫精誠篇) and later discussions of Chronic Illness
Attributed Author: Sun Simiao (孫思邈, 581–682 CE)
Original:"上工治未病。"
Translation: *"The highest skill is to treat illness before it arises."*

[51] Chen Wuze: A physician of the Song dynasty, best known for his work *Sanjin Fang* (*Formulas from the Three Categories*), which focused on classifying and treating externally contracted diseases. He contributed to the development of Warm Disease (Wen Bing) theory by distinguishing between different types of febrile disorders and emphasizing careful pattern differentiation. His work helped bridge classical Cold Damage theory with emerging approaches to epidemic and seasonal illnesses.

[52] San Yin Ji Yi Bing Zheng Fang Lun: Translated as *Treatise on the Three Causes of Diseases*, Chen Wuze wrote this Song dynasty medical classic in 1174 CE. This text systematized the concept of the *three causes* (*san yin*) of disease: internal causes (neiyin), such as emotions; external causes (waiyin), such as wind, cold, damp, or heat; and non–internal-external causes (buyin feiyin), such as improper diet, overwork, or injury. Chen Wuze emphasized the role of constitutional weakness and pathological "root vs. branch" dynamics in the progression of illness. The work is also notable for its discussion of complex, mixed pathologies and the need for formulas that address multiple mechanisms simultaneously. *San Yin Ji Yi Bing Zheng Fang Lun* influenced later Ming and Qing physicians, including Ye Tianshi, and remains an important text for understanding the early synthesis of etiological theory in Chinese medicine.

[53] Text: *Sān Yīn Jì Yī Bìng Zhèng Fāng Lùn* (三因極一病證方論)
Section: On Hidden Pathogens (伏邪篇)
Attributed Author: Chen Wuze (陳無擇, died ca. 1170)
Original: "邪氣伏而不表，當察於血。"
Translation: "When evil Qi does not manifest on the surface, one must examine the blood."

[54] Liu Wansu: A prominent Jin dynasty physician (c. 1110–1200 CE) and founder of the "Cold and Cooling School" (Han Liang Pai). He emphasized the role of fire and heat in the pathology of many diseases and advocated the use of cooling herbs to clear heat and restrain Yang. Liu Wansu reinterpreted the *Huang Di Nei Jing* to support his view that many internal diseases arose from excessive heat, laying the foundation for later developments in Warm Disease (Wen Bing) theory.

[55] Text: *Su Wen Xuan Ji Yuan Bing Shi* (素問宣明原病式)
Section: On Internal Fire and Latent Heat
Attributed Author: Liu Wansu (劉完素, 1110-1200)
Original: "火氣不除，內伏為病根。"
Translation: "When fire Qi is not extinguished, it hides within and becomes the root of disease."

[56] Zhang Congzheng: A leading physician of the Jin dynasty (1156–1228 CE) and a key figure in the "Attacking School" of medicine. He believed that most illnesses were caused by external pathogens and emphasized purging,

remain after the acute symptoms have faded.[57] Zhu Danxi[58] (1281-1358) later linked lingering heat to yin depletion, warning that "heat consumes the fluids and conceals itself in the lower burner."[59]

In the *Wen Yi Lun*[60], Wu Youke[61] (1582–1652) was the first to describe the concept of pestilential qi lingering within the boundary between the exterior and interior, creating a form of residual pathogen that persists beyond the acute stage of disease. Pestilential qi is thought to result from the retention of turbid epidemic qi between the exterior and interior. This insight laid the groundwork for modern interpretations of lingering pathogenic illness, particularly in post-viral syndromes.

---

sweating, and vomiting to expel them. Zhang advocated aggressive treatment methods to restore balance and was known for his bold, pathogen-centered approach, which contrasted with more nourishing or harmonizing styles. His work helped shape discussions around the strength of Zheng Qi versus the force of pathogenic factors.

[57] Text: *Rùmén Shìqīn* (儒門事親)
Section: On Treating Latent Disease through Expulsion
Attributed Author: Zhang Congzheng (張從正, 1156–1228)
Original: "病雖已去，而濁氣未清，當攻之。"
Translation: "Even when the disease appears to have passed, if turbid Qi has not cleared, it must be expelled."

[58] Zhu Danxi: A major physician of the Yuan dynasty (1281–1358 CE) and founder of the "Yin-Supplementing School" (Zhi Yin Pai). He emphasized that most chronic illnesses stem from Yin deficiency and the overactivity of Yang, coining the phrase "Yang is always in excess; Yin is always insufficient." Zhu promoted nourishing Yin, clearing deficiency heat, and supporting the body's essence, influencing centuries of internal medicine and gynecology. His thought marked a shift toward treating internal depletion rather than external invasion.

[59] Text: *Dàn Xī Xīn Fǎ* (丹溪心法)
Section: Discussion of Heat and Yin Depletion
Attributed Author: Zhu Danxi (朱丹溪, 1281–1358)
Original: "熱伏下焦，耗人津液。"
Translation: "Heat conceals itself in the lower burner and consumes the body's fluids."

[60] Wen Yi Lun: A foundational medical text that introduced a groundbreaking theory of epidemic illness as caused by a unique category of external pathogens called li qi - pestilential or heteropathic qi - distinct from the six climatic excesses (wind, cold, damp, etc.) traditionally emphasized in Chinese medicine. Wu Youke argued that epidemic diseases arise from specific, transmissible influences that invade the body via the mouth and nose, contradicting dominant medical views of his time. His insights laid the intellectual groundwork for later developments in warm disease (wen bing) theory and are often cited as early formulations of a contagion model within TCM. Wen Yi Lun's core legacy is its recognition of how pathogens can linger internally after the acute phase has passed - a concept that continues to inform the modern treatment of post-viral syndromes, including Long Covid.

[61] Wu Youke: A physician and medical theorist of the late Ming dynasty (1582–1652), Wu Youke is best known for authoring the *Wen Yi Lun* (*Treatise on Pestilence*), in which he proposed that epidemic diseases arise from a distinct class of pathogenic qi - li qi - that is transmissible, non-seasonal, and capable of invading through the mouth and nose. Challenging classical models that attributed illness solely to the six climatic influences, Wu laid the conceptual groundwork for understanding contagion and lingering pathogens in Chinese medicine. His work anticipated key elements of germ theory and deeply influenced the development of wen bing (warm disease) theory during the Qing dynasty.

Ye Tianshi[62] (1666-1745), the pioneer of Wen Bing theory, introduced the concept of *lurking heat*, heat that sinks into the Ying and Blood levels and does not surface until provoked by stress or seasonal change. "When heat hides," he wrote, "it appears not in fever, but in restlessness and dryness."[63]

A Qing dynasty physician known for his incisive commentary on Wen Bing theory, Yang Lishan[64] (1705-?) brought attention to the post-epidemic vulnerability of source qi and the dangers of over-aggressive treatment during recovery. His writings emphasized that the appearance of heat resolution did not always signal full recovery, cautioning that pathogenic remnants could persist in a concealed form, especially if the body's upright Qi was weak. His approach helped define a clinical stance of protection over pursuit, and his voice remains a subtle but influential thread in the classical lineage of treating lingering illness.

Wu Jutong[65] (1758-1836), in his *Wen Bing Tiao Bian*[66], clarified this further, charting the progression of febrile disease into deeper strata of the body. He

---

[62] Ye Tianshi: A leading physician of the Qing dynasty (1666–1745 CE) and a principal founder of Warm Disease (Wen Bing) theory. He developed the Four Levels model (Wei, Qi, Ying, Xue) to describe the progression of febrile illnesses caused by warm pathogens. Ye emphasized early, precise intervention to clear heat and protect Yin, and his work shifted focus from Cold Damage to epidemic febrile diseases. His clinical clarity and focus on pathogen depth continue to influence modern Chinese medicine.

[63] Text: *Wēn Rè Lùn* (溫熱論)
Section: Ying and Blood Level Patterns (營分、血分篇)
Attributed Author: Ye Tianshi (葉天士, 1666–1745)
Original: "伏熱不作熱，而作煩與燥。"
Translation: "When Heat hides, it does not manifest as fever, but as restlessness and dryness."

[64] Yang Lishan: A physician and commentator of the Qing dynasty (1705–?), Yang Lishan is known for his contributions to the interpretation and application of *wen bing* (warm disease) theory. He emphasized the importance of preserving source qi during and after febrile illness, warning against overuse of purgatives and excessive cooling therapies in weakened patients. Yang recognized that pathogens could linger in a concealed state, and advocated for a treatment strategy that balanced clearing heat with supporting the body's upright qi. His clinical sensibility brought nuance to the evolving epidemic disease discourse and helped shape a more restrained, qi-preserving approach to unresolved or post-acute illness.

[65] Wu Jutong: A Qing dynasty physician (1758–1836 CE) known for systematizing Warm Disease (Wen Bing) theory through his influential text *Wen Bing Tiao Bian* (*Systematic Differentiation of Warm Diseases*). He introduced the concept of the Membrane Source (Mo Yuan) as a key site where warm pathogens lodge, leading to lingering or relapsing illness. Wu emphasized early cooling and venting to prevent deep penetration of heat, and his work helped refine the diagnosis and treatment of epidemic febrile diseases and latent pathogens.

[66] Wen Bing Tiao Bian: Translated as *Detailed Analysis of Warm Diseases*, an influential Qing dynasty medical classic written by Wu Jutong and published in 1798 CE. The text systematized the theory of Warm Diseases (Wen Bing) - febrile epidemics caused by externally contracted "warm pathogens." Wu Jutong elaborated the *Four Levels* (Wei, Qi, Ying, Xue) as a framework for understanding the depth and progression of pathogenic heat, and he provided corresponding formulas for each stage, many of which remain standards in clinical practice (e.g., Yin Qiao San, Qing Ying Tang, Xi Jiao Di Huang Tang). The work marks a shift from the *Shang Han Lun*'s six-stage model

documented Ye Tianshi's system of Wei, Qi, Ying, and Blood, which became one of the clearest maps for tracking lingering disease, especially in modern chronic inflammatory patterns.[67] We will explore this system, the Four Levels, in much greater detail in Chapter 3.

Jiang Baosu[68] (1794–1873), writing in the mid-19th century, advanced the theory of lingering pathogenic illness by articulating a detailed framework for understanding "fu xie," or latent pathogenic factors. In his *Yilüe Yizhong Jiyan*[69], he systematized this concept to describe evils that evade immediate detection, remaining concealed in the body despite symptomatic resolution. Jiang documented clinical cases where disease did not progress through the expected stages but instead lingered silently, later reemerging as complex, chronic illness. He emphasized the critical role of Zheng Qi[70] (upright Qi) in containing or failing to suppress

> **Zheng Qi or "Upright Qi"**
>
> Zheng Qi is a composite of all the physiological Qi in the body, including Wei Qi, or that of the immune system.
>
> When Zheng Qi is adequate throughout infection or injury, the patient fully recovers. When Zheng Qi is severely compromised, the patient does not recover.

of cold damage to a specialized theory of epidemic febrile disease, reflecting new clinical realities of the Qing period. *Wen Bing Tiao Bian* is considered the definitive text of the Warm Disease school, and its diagnostic structure continues to shape both modern Chinese medicine and integrative approaches to infectious disease.

[67] Text: *Wēn Bìng Tiáo Biàn* (溫病條辨)
Section: General Introduction and Commentary on Four-Level Differentiation (四層辨證總論)
Attributed Author: Wu Jutong (吳鞠通, 1758–1836)
Original: "衛氣營血辨證，條分縷析，以明病之淺深。"
Translation: "The differentiation of Wei, Qi, Ying, and Blood allows for precise analysis of the depth and progression of disease."

[68] Jiang Baosu: Qing dynasty physician best known for his work *Yixue Yizhong Jiyan* ("Collected Medical Insights from Doubts in Medicine"). Jiang is notable for his careful clinical observations and emphasis on unresolved or atypical disease patterns—especially those that defied straightforward diagnostic categories. His case studies reflect a deep concern for illnesses that linger or transform over time, and his writings frequently reference the importance of treating what is hidden or obscured. Jiang's work serves as a bridge between classical theory and modern clinical complexity, preserving the legacy of lingering pathogenic illness as a legitimate and central concern of Chinese medicine.

[69] Yilüe Yizhong Jiyan or "*Collected Medical Insights from Doubts in Medicine*": A compilation of clinical reflections by Jiang Baosu (1794–1873). The text emphasizes case-based reasoning and unresolved pathologies, reflecting Jiang's deep engagement with lingering and atypical illnesses. It was originally compiled in the mid-19th century and remains a valuable source for Qing dynasty clinical thinking.

[70] Zheng Qi: Upright or righteous Qi - an umbrella term encompassing all protective and regulatory forces of the body, including Wei Qi, Ying Qi, and Yuan Qi. It is the body's capacity to resist and recover from illness. When Zheng Qi is weak, pathogenic factors may lodge or linger, leading to chronic illness.

these hidden evils, warning that weakened constitutional strength allowed fu xie to deepen and transform. His work not only preserved but refined classical Warm Disease and Cold Damage logic, offering a clinically relevant bridge to the persistent, relapsing disorders increasingly seen in his own time, and in ours.

In the early 20th century, Liu Bao-Yi[71] (1842-1901) brought Lingering Pathogenic Illness into the modern medical conversation. He coined the term *fú xíe*, or "residual evil," and insisted that "Lingering pathogens are such a common illness. It is recorded in the *Nei Jing*, *Nan Jing*, and *Shang Han Lun*, and thus not a weird theory."[72] He described how patients who never fully recover from fevers often develop a wide range of chronic complaints, palpitations, fatigue, dry throat, low-grade fever, that resist typical treatment.

Though not the first to do so, Liu Bao-Yi heavily emphasized the need to protect the body from damage caused by Lingering Pathogenic Illness. He argued that the very aspects of the body damaged by lingering pathogenic heat are also those required to resolve the illness, and therefore must be restored as part of treatment.

An erudite reformist of the late Qing dynasty, Zhou Xuehai[73] is remembered for his deep insights into the incomplete resolution of febrile disease. He argued that illness often hides beneath the surface, particularly in the aftermath of febrile conditions, when the heat appears to resolve but continues to smolder internally. His writings,

---

[71] Liu Bao-Yi: A 19th-century physician and prominent advocate of the nourishing school in the late Qing dynasty. Known for emphasizing the importance of supporting Zheng Qi (upright or righteous Qi) rather than over-relying on harsh methods to expel pathogens, Liu famously argued that "in treating disease, one must first nourish the body's strength; only then can one expel the evil." His approach prioritized gentle, restorative treatment—especially in chronic or deficiency conditions—and stands as a counterpoint to more aggressive schools of thought in Chinese medicine.

[72] Text: *Wēn Rè Fēng Yuán* (溫熱逢原)
Section: Treatise on Residual Pathogens (論伏邪病)
Attributed Author: Liu Bao-Yi (劉保儀, 1842–1901)
Original: "伏邪之病，最為常見，《內經》《難經》《傷寒》皆有之，非奇說也。"
Translation: "Lingering pathogens are a very common illness. They are recorded in the *Nei Jing*, *Nan Jing*, and *Shang Han Lun*; this is not a strange theory."

[73] Zhou Xuehai: A physician and scholar of the late Qing dynasty (1856–1906), Zhou Xuehai is best known for his critical engagement with *wen bing* theory and his nuanced exploration of lingering and hidden disease mechanisms. In his influential text *Wen Bing Zong Lun* (*Comprehensive Treatise on Warm Diseases*), he emphasized the role of latent heat, membrane source (mo yuan) pathology, and the incomplete resolution of febrile illnesses. Zhou warned that heat may appear to disperse externally while continuing to smolder within, particularly when the pulse and spirit do not reflect true resolution. His clinical observations helped formalize a framework for understanding persistent, unresolved illness, bridging classical models with presentations now associated with post-viral and inflammatory syndromes.

especially in the *Wen Bing Zong Lun*[74], highlight the danger of relying solely on external signs of improvement and stress the need to treat the hidden dynamics of lingering pathogenic Qi. Zhou's clinical vision foresaw many of the presentations now associated with post-viral syndromes, making his work strikingly relevant to the current landscape of unresolved and relapsing illness.

These physicians offer us something more than scattered case notes or historical curiosities, they offer an alternate route. When chronic conditions fail to resolve through conventional treatments, these lineages become a map. Lingering Pathogenic Illness is not a codified school of thought, but a centuries-long conversation carried out across texts, dynasties, and clinics. It is a scattered lineage, but a real one. In its disjointed brilliance lies an insight that modern medicine often misses: not all illness ends predictably, and recovery is not guaranteed. These ancient frameworks offer us tools to approach the unresolved, the cyclical, the inflammatory, and the invisible with fresh eyes.

In our own era, modern practitioners have rediscovered this lineage. They use it to address persistent viral syndromes, Long Lyme, Myalgic Encephalomyelitis, Long Covid, and a host of unnamed, misnamed, or ignored illnesses. They help give shape to the elusive, using classical logic to explain contemporary suffering.

This history is not just intellectual scaffolding. It's a statement of legitimacy. It says: there is nothing strange about what we are seeing. We are part of a lineage that has always recognized what lingers, hides, and waits. And we actually have tools to meet it.

---

[74] Wen Bing Zong Lun: *Comprehensive Treatise on Warm Diseases*, this late Qing dynasty text by Zhou Xuehai (1856–1906) synthesized and critiqued centuries of *wen bing* (warm disease) theory. Drawing from earlier thinkers such as Wu Youke and Wu Jutong, Zhou offered a refined clinical framework for the diagnosis and treatment of febrile illnesses, latent heat, and lingering pathogenic conditions. He emphasized the importance of pulse-spirit discordance, membrane source pathology, and the danger of superficial resolution that conceals deeper, unresolved heat. The *Wen Bing Zong Lun* represents a mature evolution of epidemic disease theory in Chinese medicine and remains an important reference for understanding chronic post-febrile syndromes.

Chapter Two: Contributing Causes and Environmental Factors

Now that we've established a historical foundation for Lingering Pathogenic Illness (LPI), we can turn to its etiology. In this chapter, we'll explore the various causes of LPI, introduce a framework known as the Eight Depressions, and review its common symptoms and triggers.

Lingering Pathogenic Illness is not simply the convalescent stage of infection. Rather, it is the unresolved injury that infection (or other trauma) leaves behind, which may or may not include an actual persistent infection. Though sometimes acute, the initial injury is usually an insidious phenomenon. It is slow, layered, and deeply influenced by the terrain it enters. It embeds not only into flesh and fluids, but also into deeper lymphoid tissues of the lungs, gut, central nervous system(CNS), and bone.

LPI behaves as a syndrome of stagnation and deficiency: dampness[75] that never resolves, phlegm[76] that never clears, Qi[77], Yin[78], and Yang[79] that never recover. But among these pathological factors lie more subtle wounds, wounds that afflict the adaptive interface between the body's defenses and its internal environment.

In classical language, this can mean that the Wei Qi[80] and Zheng Qi[81] have been injured or drained. It can mean that the Taiyang[82] surface or the Shaoyang pivot may have been breached. Or it can mean that the pathogen has bypassed early defenses entirely and rooted directly into the Ying[83] or Blood[84] levels, where it distorts recovery even further.

---

[75] Dampness(TCM): A heavy, turbid, and obstructive pathogenic factor that impairs Qi movement and fluid transformation. It can be external (from the environment) or internal (from Spleen dysfunction). Symptoms include fatigue, brain fog, loose stools, heaviness, and mucus. In biomedical terms, Dampness corresponds to metabolic waste accumulation, cytokine load, or lymphatic stagnation.

[76] Phlegm(TCM): A congealed form of Dampness that obstructs the body more deeply, particularly the channels or sensory orifices. It may be visible (e.g., sputum, nodules) or invisible (e.g., brain fog, mental confusion, systemic inflammation). In chronic illness, Phlegm is often seen in neuroinflammatory states, lipid dysregulation, and immune overactivation.

[77] Qi: The vital energy that powers all physiological processes in the body. It can be categorized as Wei Qi (defensive), Ying Qi (nutritive), or Yuan Qi (source/original). In chronic illness, Qi may become deficient, stagnant, or blocked. Qi is mostly intangible and used as a descriptor of measurement to define how well various systems are functioning in the body.

[78] Yin: The nourishing, cooling, and restorative counterpart to Yang. Yin encompasses bodily fluids, Blood, Essence, and the structural and regenerative substrates of the body. Yin deficiency manifests as dryness, heat signs, restlessness, or insomnia. Biomedically, Yin is linked to parasympathetic tone, neuroendocrine reserves, and cellular repair capacity.

[79] Yang: The dynamic, warming, and active aspect of the Yin-Yang pair. Yang governs function, movement, transformation, and defense. Deficiency of Yang may present as cold limbs, fatigue, poor metabolism, or sluggish immunity. In biomedical analogues, Yang is often associated with mitochondrial output, hormonal activation, and thermoregulation.

[80] Wei Qi: The body's defensive Qi, circulating on the surface and guarding against external pathogens. It governs immune vigilance, temperature regulation, and circadian rhythm. Weak Wei Qi can result in frequent infections, allergies, or hypersensitivities. Often compared to innate immunity.

[81] Zheng Qi: Upright or righteous Qi - an umbrella term encompassing all protective and regulatory forces of the body, including Wei Qi, Ying Qi, and Yuan Qi. It is the body's capacity to resist and recover from illness. When Zheng Qi is weak, pathogenic factors may lodge or linger, leading to chronic illness.

[82] Taiyang: The most external of the six stages, governing the Bladder and Small Intestine channels. Often the first to respond to external invasion. In Lingering Illness, unresolved Taiyang-stage disorders may sink deeper or recur.

[83] Ying Level: The nutritive (Ying) Qi layer, reflecting deeper heat affecting the Heart and Pericardium. Symptoms include fever worse at night, restlessness, insomnia, dry mouth, and sometimes faint rashes or delirium. The tongue is deep red or crimson, and the pulse is thin and rapid. This level indicates that heat is beginning to injure Yin and disturb the Shen (spirit).

[84] Blood Level: The deepest level, where heat has penetrated the Blood layer, causing reckless movement of Blood or extreme internal heat. Signs include high fever, bleeding (e.g., nosebleeds, blood in stool), rashes, delirium,

LPI behaves like a burrowing influence, moving from exterior to interior, from Yang to Yin, from abundant to deficient systems. It descends into areas of pre-existing weakness, especially where channel integrity is compromised. A person with Liver[85] stagnation may develop hypersensitivities or blood heat. A person with Spleen[86] deficiency may develop postprandial fatigue, loose stools, or gut autoimmunity. A person with Shaoyin Cold may become severely Yang deficient.

Thus, LPI cannot be mapped by symptoms alone. It must be understood as a dynamic, layered deficiency and disturbance, not just of Wei Qi(Defensive Qi), but of underpinning physiology. And while it mimics simpler presentations, such as Yin deficiency, toxic heat, or phlegm misting the Heart, it always speaks of something deeper and more complex: a failed resolution due to a failure of multiple systems.

Etiologies of Lingering Pathogenic Illness

Lingering Pathogenic Illness rarely arises from a singular cause. It is more often the product of accumulated insults: overlapping injuries to the immune system, constitution, and the body's capacity to resolve and recover.

The following categories represent the most common propensities and insults through which lingering pathogens embed and persist. Although presented separately, these etiologies frequently overlap in real patients, reflecting the complex nature of modern chronic illnesses.

---

convulsions, and a deep red or crimson tongue. This stage often involves Yin collapse and severe Shen disturbance, requiring urgent intervention.

[85] Liver(TCM/organ/channel): Ensures the smooth flow of Qi and stores Blood. Imbalances may lead to stagnation, irritability, menstrual irregularity, or tendinomuscular tension. Also central to detoxification and the emotional interface of chronic illness.

[86] Spleen(TCM/organ/channel): Transforms food into Qi and Blood, governs the muscles, and holds Blood in the vessels. Spleen Qi deficiency often underlies fatigue, poor digestion, edema, and chronic illness patterns involving Dampness.

Deficiency of Zheng Qi (Constitutional or Acquired)

Whether from birth(pre-natal Qi[87]), chronic depletion, or failure to rest during illness, a deficiency in Spleen, Lung[88], or Kidney[89] Qi weakens the body's ability to contain or expel pathogens.[90] The terrain is unprotected, and the pathogen is not fully cleared; it lingers, sinks deeper, and embeds. Historically, Zhang Zhongjing described "taxation relapse" as an illness that lingers due to failure to rest, a pattern commonly observed in modern patients with Long Covid and/or ME/CFS.

Unresolved Pathogenic Challenge

In some cases, the pathogen is simply too strong for the host's defenses, such as an immune-evasive virus, or an immune challenge (like vaccination) introduced into a weakened terrain. Without proper immune containment and drainage, the pathogen (or its residue) remains lodged, *often unnoticed* until perturbed, and chronic symptoms emerge.

Iatrogenic Disruption of Resolution

Improper treatment, whether antibiotic overuse, suppressive pharmaceuticals, or improper purging/tonification, can drive a pathogen deeper into the body or damage the systems needed for resolution. As with all cases of Lingering Pathogenic Illness, it is not necessarily an offending pathogen that causes the illness, but the loss of

---

[87] Pre-natal Qi: The foundational life force inherited at conception, derived from the essence of the parents. Pre-natal Qi is stored in the Kidneys and forms the basis of one's constitutional strength, vitality, and longevity. It governs growth, development, and the capacity for regeneration. Unlike Post-natal Qi, which is replenished through food, breath, and experience, Pre-natal Qi is finite and non-renewable—though it can be conserved and supported through careful lifestyle and treatment strategies. In modern terms, it parallels aspects of genetic inheritance, mitochondrial vigor, and baseline immune resilience.

[88] Lung(TCM/organ/channel): Governs respiration, Wei Qi (defensive energy), and fluid metabolism. Frequently the first system affected by external pathogens. In chronic illness, the Lung often suffers from residual heat, phlegm, or dryness.

[89] Kidney(TCM/organ/channel): Stores Essence and governs growth, reproduction, and water metabolism. The Kidney is the foundation of Yin and Yang and supports the marrow, brain, and bones. Often implicated in chronic fatigue, endocrine disorders, and degenerative illness.

[90] Lyttleton, Jane, and William Maclean. *Clinical Handbook of Internal Medicine: The Treatment of Disease with Traditional Chinese Medicine, Vol. 3: Qi, Blood, Fluid and Channel Disorders*. Seattle: Eastland Press, 2019.

antigenic tone that allows non-self to persist and/or reactivate (more on this in Chapter4).

Pharmaceutical and Recreational Drug Use

Many pharmaceuticals, especially stimulants, weaken or confuse immune function.[91] In classical terms, they damage Shaoyin, weaken Kidney fire, and disrupt the heart-spirit axis. This creates internal confusion, rendering the system unable to properly identify or eliminate latent pathogens.

Environmental Exposure

Exposure to damp, toxic, or mold-laden environments can wear down the Spleen, destabilize the Wei Qi, and create an internal terrain that favors pathogen embedding. These exposures also impair liver detoxification[92], membrane source[93] integrity, and gut immune coordination.

Emotional Trauma and Chronic Stress

Emotional injuries, especially grief, shock, or prolonged anxiety, can damage the Heart-Kidney axis and Spleen-Lung Qi, creating multiple internal weak points. These are common in patients with LPI who "crashed" after a divorce, loss, trauma, or long-term caregiving burden.

---

[91] Lyttleton, Jane, and William Maclean. *Clinical Handbook of Internal Medicine: The Treatment of Disease with Traditional Chinese Medicine, Vol. 3: Qi, Blood, Fluid and Channel Disorders*. Seattle: Eastland Press, 2019.

[92] Liver Detoxification: The liver's process of transforming and clearing toxins, hormones, and metabolic waste through Phase I (modification), Phase II (conjugation), and bile elimination. This system relies on nutrients like B vitamins and glutathione. Impaired detox can lead to toxin buildup—especially from sources like mold—which may contribute to inflammation, hormonal imbalance, and fatigue. In Chinese medicine, it parallels the Liver's role in coursing Qi and resolving internal constraint.

[93] Mo Yuan(Membrane Source): A classical Chinese medical concept describing an intermediate space between interior and exterior. Pathogens lodged here are neither fully in nor fully out, leading to low-grade, chronic, or relapsing illness. Often involved in Shaoyang patterns and post-viral syndromes.

LPI doesn't begin as a mystery; it begins as a failure of resolution in the presence of vulnerability. These vulnerabilities may be constitutional, iatrogenic, emotional, environmental, or immune-related, but they all share one trait: they leave behind a terrain in which pathogens don't fully exit.

Understanding etiology in these terms allows the clinician to trace back the breach, identifying not just the initial invader but also the conditions that may have allowed it, or something else, to persist.

The Six Depressions

Why am I choosing to talk about the Six Depressions in a chapter on etiology? Areas of stagnation in the body are not just the result of Lingering Pathogenic Illness; they can also be a precipitating cause, and/or exacerbate the illness. For that reason, it is best that we cover this concept now rather than later.

Lingering Pathogenic Illness rarely arises from a single source. It is the product of layered assaults on a system already compromised by trauma, diet, climate, microbial burden, emotional strain, and constitutional vulnerability. To understand the climate in which lingering evils take root, we turn first to the classical lens of the Six Depressions, a systematized view of how pathogenic obstructions express themselves.

Originally articulated by Zhu Danxi and further developed by Ye Tianshi and others, the Six Depressions identify six primary forms of stagnation that can entrap evil Qi within the body. The following are the canonical Six Depressions, a few additions, and their symptoms:

1. Qi depression - emotional suppression, stagnation of movement
2. Blood depression - trauma, menstrual irregularity, clotting, pain
3. Damp depression - heaviness, fatigue, internal obstruction
4. Phlegm depression - nodules, brain fog, chronic mucus
5. Fire depression - hidden heat, irritability, latent fever
6. Food depression - digestive burden, food retention
7. [Cold depression - internal cold, pain, poor circulation]
8. [Summerheat depression - residual heat exhaustion]

9. [Fright - emotional trauma, scattering of function][94]

These are not distinct "diseases," but expressions of a body unable to resolve what it has absorbed. In the context of lingering illness, these depressions act like climatic dead zones, zones where the pathogen cannot be released, and where the body's internal rhythms are disrupted.

Many LPI patients present with multiple forms of depression: phlegm damp with heat and blood stasis[95], phlegm damp with cold, or heat with blood stasis. Over time, these states congeal into a terrain favorable to latency. They create the conditions where an external pathogenic factor cannot be fully cleared, or where the remnants of an illness become embedded in the tissues.

Common Symptoms of Lingering Pathogenic Illness

Symptoms of Lingering Pathogenic Illness can range from relatively benign to severe, disabling, and life-threatening. Some patients are able to manage symptoms with pacing and avoiding certain triggers, while others are completely at the mercy of their disease. The following symptoms, though most common, are not a full picture of Lingering Pathogenic Illness but offer insight into what patients most commonly experience.

Low-Grade Fever or Temperature Instability

Persistent low-grade fevers, tidal fevers, or those worse at night and/or after exertion can be a hallmark of lingering illness. Patients may experience subjective heat

---

[94] Text: *Dàn Xī Xīn Fǎ* (丹溪心法)
Section: On the Eight Depressions (八鬱篇)
Attributed Author: Zhu Danxi (朱丹溪, 1281–1358); elaborated by Ye Tianshi (葉天士) and others
Original: "鬱有八端：氣、血、濕、痰、食、火、暑、驚。"
Translation: "There are eight forms of constraint: Qi, Blood, Dampness, Phlegm, Food, Fire, Summer-Heat, and Fright." The bracketed depressions are those which were not considered to be the original six(or eight) but are often included by later physicians.

[95] Blood Stasis(TCM): A pathological condition where Blood fails to flow smoothly, resulting in stagnation. It may manifest as fixed, sharp pain, dark or purplish complexion or tongue, or palpable masses. In chronic illness, Blood Stasis often reflects inflammation, circulatory impairment, or unresolved tissue damage. It is also metaphorically linked to emotional trauma and immune rigidity.

effusion (flushing and heat aversion) or objective (persistent low-grade fever). Patients may be cold in the morning, cold in the lower half of their body, or cold all over due to dampness (more damp than heat), in which case the heat or fever is "contained" and only surfaces when provoked (by new infection/exposure, trigger, or even treatment). Patients may be particularly sensitive to heat *and* cold and experience an exacerbation of other symptoms after exposure to either extreme (dizziness, itching, etc.). In the case of alternating heat effusion and aversion to cold in acute illness, the heat is thought to be the patient's Zheng or upright Qi fighting off the pathogen, while the cold is the pathogen prevailing.

Weak Voice and Taciturnity

A weak or low voice, along with a tendency toward quietness or reluctance to speak (taciturnity), often reflects a deficiency of Lung or Spleen Qi. Patients may report fatigue after speaking or a sense that speaking requires effort. This can be especially pronounced after exertion or during flares, and is a subtle but telling sign of Qi depletion. In classical Chinese medicine, "less speech" and "low voice" are diagnostic of a weakened Qi dynamic, particularly in post-viral or chronically depleted states. These symptoms are sometimes misattributed to mood or affect, but should instead prompt inquiry into constitutional or acquired weakness. The loss of verbal vitality may also correlate with poor respiratory or digestive capacity and warrants treatment focused on restoring core Qi.

Muscle and Joint Pain or Weakness

LPI patients often report experiencing achiness, heaviness, or fatigue in their muscles and joints. These symptoms are often diagnosed as fibromyalgia or dismissed as "deconditioning," when in fact they reflect more profound obstruction. The heaviness and the joint aches are more so a product of dampness accruing in the limbs, usually most noticeable in the lower limbs but sometimes the upper as well. The rapid fatigue of muscles throughout the body is a product of stagnant heat. Most Lingering Pathogenic Illness patients have a combination of dampness and heat, while some present one climatic factor more than the other. In biomedical terms, dampness can be thought of as an excess of fluid or ionic imbalance, while heat is associated with lactic acid, dead blood, and oxidative stress.

Intractable Fatigue

This is perhaps one of the most common symptoms across all cases of chronic Lingering Pathogenic Illness. The fatigue is consumptive; it is minimally improved by rest and usually worsens with exertion (mental and/or physical) and/or exposure to environmental toxins, such as mold. Fatigue triggered by exertion can have an onset ranging from a few hours to a full day after the triggering activity and can last anywhere from a day to weeks or longer. Patients with ME, and practitioners who treat it, refer to post-exertional fatigue as post-exertional malaise (PEM)[96] or post-exertional neuroimmune exhaustion(PENE). There is no acronym for post-exposure (mold, etc) malaise[97], which can have an immediate onset, but it is widely recognized within patient communities and among practitioners. A similar acronym, PESE[98] (post-exertional symptom exacerbation), is used to describe the exacerbation of any number of chronic symptoms by exertion, not just debilitating fatigue.

In Chinese medicine, somnolence or the "desire only to sleep" is most often seen during PEM crashes or chronic Shaoyin level Lingering Pathogenic Illness in which the body's physiological heat or Yang has been severely damaged("Cold Transformation"). However, "desire only to sleep" can also show up in relapsing forms of enduring Taiyang pathology, in which the body begs for rest to continually re-assert and recover Zheng or upright, and Wei or defensive Qi. In Chapter 6, I

---

96 Post-Exertional Malaise (PEM): A hallmark symptom of ME/CFS and Long Covid characterized by a delayed worsening of symptoms (e.g., fatigue, pain, brain fog) following physical or mental exertion. PEM reflects metabolic inflexibility, mitochondrial dysfunction, and immune exhaustion. In Chinese medicine, it correlates with Qi and Yin deficiency compounded by latent pathogenic activity.

97 Post-Exposure Malaise (e.g., Mold): An acute or delayed worsening of symptoms following exposure to environmental triggers like mold, chemicals, or allergens. Often seen in patients with mast cell activation, dysautonomia, or persistent immune activation. In TCM, it suggests Lingering Pathogen reactivation combined with Wind-Damp invasion and Wei Qi instability.

98 Post-Exertional Symptom Exacerbation (PESE): A broader term than post-exertional malaise (PEM), PESE refers to the worsening of a range of symptoms - not only fatigue - following physical, cognitive, or emotional exertion. These may include pain, orthostatic intolerance, immune flares, or neurocognitive dysfunction. PESE highlights the multisystem dysregulation underlying Long Covid and ME/CFS, including immune activation, impaired metabolic recovery, and autonomic instability. In Chinese medicine, PESE is understood as the destabilization of latent pathogens and dysregulation of Wei and Ying Qi coordination in response to strain on a deficient system.

suggest a modified Shen Qi Wan for "Cold Transformation" somnolence, and a modified Gui Zhi Jia Huang Qi Tang for Taiyang somnolence.

Dizziness and Lightheadedness

Often diagnosed as postural hypotension[99] or another form of dysautonomia[100], dizziness experienced in Lingering Pathogenic Illness is usually caused by heat in specific channels (Shaoyang, Jueyin) in Chinese medicine. Patients may still experience dizziness related to hypotension or POTS[101] as part of Lingering Pathogenic Illness, but it is typically due to blood stasis, Qi, and/or Blood deficiency. Dizziness that doesn't coincide with dysautonomia is caused by heat coursing through particular channels of the body, which can be caused by exposure (to heat), exertion, mast cell activation[102], and hot or warming food.

"*Veiling (dizziness) is obstruction. Precipitation*[103] *results in interior Qi and Blood deficiency. Venting*[104] *results in exterior Qi and Yang deficiency. When the exterior*

[99] Orthostatic Hypotension (OH): A form of dysautonomia where blood pressure drops significantly upon standing, often leading to dizziness, lightheadedness, or syncope. Common in chronic fatigue syndromes, OH reflects impaired vascular tone and autonomic regulation. In TCM, it may reflect Qi, Yang, or Blood deficiency.

[100] Dysautonomia: A broad term describing dysfunction of the autonomic nervous system (ANS), which regulates involuntary functions like heart rate, blood pressure, digestion, and temperature. Symptoms may include dizziness, palpitations, GI disturbance, fatigue, and thermoregulatory issues. Common in Long Covid, ME/CFS, and other chronic inflammatory syndromes, dysautonomia is often secondary to immune or barrier dysfunction and can reflect deeper Qi and Yin depletion in Chinese medicine.

[101] Postural Orthostatic Tachycardia Syndrome (POTS): A form of dysautonomia marked by an excessive heart rate increase upon standing (typically >30 bpm in adults, >40 bpm in adolescents), often accompanied by lightheadedness, palpitations, and fatigue. POTS is frequently seen in Long Covid and ME/CFS and is associated with hypovolemia, immune activation, mast cell dysfunction, and neurovascular dysregulation.

[102] Mast Cell Activation Syndrome (MCAS): A condition in which mast cells release histamine and other mediators inappropriately, causing symptoms like flushing, rashes, digestive upset, brain fog, and anaphylaxis. MCAS often occurs alongside chronic infections, Long Covid, and connective tissue disorders. It reflects a state of immune hyper-reactivity and disrupted homeostasis, sometimes linked to loss of inhibitory FcγR signaling and barrier dysfunction.

[103] Precipitation (xià): A specific form of draining that forcefully expels accumulation or pathogens through the bowels. Distinguished by its strong downward action, it targets interior excess—such as heat, food, or blood stasis—and is used selectively when blockage is pronounced.

[104] Venting (tòu): is the method of opening surface or intermediary layers to release trapped or latent pathogens. It facilitates the outward movement of heat, toxins, or unresolved inflammation—often through the skin, sweat, or respiration—without forceful purgation. Venting is used when blockage is not fully interiorized and may accompany mild tonification or harmonization to prevent reburial.

and interior Qi are both vacuous, the evil Qi gets stuck (the clear Yang Qi cannot ascend), and as a result, the person experiences veiling (dizziness)."

-Cheng Wu-Ji[105] (12th Century)

In Cheng Wu-Ji's above anecdote, the proper treatment of "veiling" or dizziness must entail tonification of Qi while simultaneously venting the exterior and precipitating. This is a classic example of a pathogen becoming entrenched and causing persistent symptoms until the underlying deficiency is resolved, a recurring theme throughout this book.

Rashes and/or Itching

The skin is both a pathologic and therapeutic site of expression for Lingering Pathogenic Illnesses. Generally speaking, a severe or worsening rash is an indication of a Lingering Pathogenic Illness that is aggravated or worsening (due to exertion, exposure, or another trigger). A sparse, faint, or brief rash is indicative of a Lingering Pathogenic Illness that is improving (likely due to treatment). Due to dysregulation of Ying and Wei[106], body temperature, Qi deficiency, and subsequent venous insufficiency[107], the pores may not open and close appropriately, leading to itching aggravated by exertion and/or hot and warming foods.

Bloating and Indigestion

---

[105] Cheng Wu Ji:A prominent physician and commentator of the Song dynasty (12th century), Chéng Wǔ Jí is best known for his authoritative annotations on Zhang Zhongjing's *Shāng Hán Lùn* and *Jīn Guì Yào Lüè*. His edition of the *Shāng Hán Lùn* became the basis for the "Song edition," which remains the most widely transmitted version of the text. Chéng emphasized precise pattern differentiation and the correct matching of formulas to clearly defined clinical presentations, helping standardize and preserve classical doctrine during a period of textual instability. His work continues to shape the interpretation and clinical use of Zhang Zhongjing's teachings.

[106] Dysregulation of Ying and Wei (TCM): In Chinese medicine, Ying Qi (Nutritive Qi) and Wei Qi (Defensive Qi) must harmonize to maintain health. Ying circulates in the interior, nourishing organs and tissues, while Wei circulates on the surface, protecting against external invasion. Dysregulation—often from chronic infection, overexertion, or latent pathogens—can result in immune confusion, manifesting as alternating fevers and chills, sleep disruption, or autoimmune-like patterns. In LPI, it reflects a loss of coordination between containment and expression of immune function.

[107] Venous Insufficiency: A condition where blood flow from the legs back to the heart is impaired due to weakened or damaged vein valves. This leads to pooling of blood, swelling, heaviness, and often **itching**, especially around the ankles or lower legs. Chronic cases may cause skin discoloration, irritation, or ulceration. In Chinese medicine, it may relate to blood stasis and damp accumulation in the lower Jiao.

Bloating, distention, and impaired digestion are common signs of lingering illness, often indicative of Spleen Qi deficiency, damp accumulation, or dysfunction in the Liver-Spleen axis. Patients may experience fullness in the upper or middle abdomen, gas, belching, sluggish digestion, or loss of appetite. Symptoms can fluctuate with stress, exertion, or dietary intake, particularly with cold, raw, greasy, or hard-to-digest foods. In some cases, bloating worsens throughout the day, suggesting a weakening of the Spleen's transformative and transportive functions over time. Digestive discomfort may also reflect a mismatch between upright Qi and lingering pathogenic factors (e.g., heat, phlegm, dampness) obstructing the middle burner. In lingering illness states such as ME/CFS or Long Covid, this often overlaps with microbiome disruption, vagal tone dysregulation, or inflammatory signaling within the gut-brain axis.

Common Triggers of Lingering Pathogenic Illness

Lingering Pathogenic Illness is not merely initiated by external pathogens, but it is sustained and exacerbated by a variety of triggers that tax the body's resilience. Many of these triggers overlap with the etiology itself, revealing the cyclical and persistent nature of the disease pattern.

Exertion

Exertion, whether physical, mental, or emotional, is one of the most common and consistent triggers. In TCM, physical exertion depletes Qi and Blood; mental strain scatters the Shen(Spirit) and injures the Heart and Spleen; and emotional turmoil disrupts Liver Qi. In the context of LPI, the immune system is already overburdened, and exertion often provokes relapses, seen today in phenomena like post-exertional malaise (PEM).

Environmental Factors

Environmental factors, such as seasonal or climatic change and exposure to toxins, also play a major role. Wind, Cold, Damp, and Heat, pathogenic concepts in Chinese medicine, can aggravate or awaken latent diseases, especially in a body already weakened by hidden pathogens. Damp climates exacerbate fatigue and mental fog; cold weather may induce body pain or digestive upset; and internal heat triggered by stress or external exposure can lead to inflammation, digestive issues, or skin eruptions. In modern terms, environmental toxins, mold, pollution, and chemicals are often implicated in reactivating underlying illness and creating systemic immune flares. These act like the toxic influences or "Gu" of classical medicine: external poisons that disrupt internal harmony and sink deeper into tissues over time.

Iatrogenic Factors

Iatrogenic factors, interventions that originate in the medical system, can also destabilize those with LPI. While vaccinations and pharmaceuticals are essential for many, in a vulnerable system, they may trigger hyperactivation or suppression of immune function. Vaccines, for example, can sometimes stimulate a flare of symptoms or reawaken dormant infections. Antibiotics, while life-saving, may damage the microbiome or Spleen function, creating fertile ground for fungal overgrowth and gut permeability. Other medications, such as steroids, may interfere with detoxification, digestion, or immune modulation. From a classical perspective, excessively cooling or sedating substances weaken Wei Qi and Yang, potentially allowing hidden evils to reemerge.

Infection

Finally, infection itself remains a primary catalyst for LPI progression. New infections can awaken old ones, viral, bacterial, or fungal, and further disorganize the immune landscape. In 2020, researchers at the University of Birmingham discovered that viral infection can trigger fungal persistence by altering macrophage function.[108] In TCM, this is akin to evils that were never fully expelled and now

[108] Seoane, Paula I., et al. "Viral Infection Triggers Interferon-Induced Expulsion of Live Cryptococcus Neoformans by Macrophages." *PLOS Pathogens*, Public Library of Science, journals.plos.org/plospathogens/article?id=10.1371%2Fjournal.ppat.1008240. Accessed 19 June 2025.

transform and burrow deeper into the body. Modern research into ME and Long Covid suggests that antigen-presenting cells become exhausted or dysfunctional, unable to clear new threats effectively. As a result, viral residue accumulates, triggering low-grade systemic inflammation, immune intolerance, and auto-reactivity.

Taken together, these triggers illustrate that Lingering Pathogenic Illness is a dynamic, progressive condition. It does not simply "go away" with time, nor does it conform to neat diagnostic boxes. It reactivates and evolves through interaction with the world, and demands an approach that understands both its internal and external provocateurs.

A Note on the PM VEINS Model

Later in this book, I'll return to a framework I call PM VEINS, a layered acronym describing the core pathophysiological forces behind Lingering Pathogenic Illness.

- Persistence of pathogen or immune complexes
- Metabolic reprogramming
- Vascular dysfunction
- Exhaustion (immune)
- Intolerance (mold, histamine, food, etc)
- Neuroinflammation
- Suppression (antigen presentation, HPA-axis, mitochondrial)

These factors are not separate; they interlock, amplify one another, and help explain why chronic illness is so difficult to unwind. Later chapters will map these mechanisms more precisely to immunological dysfunction and Chinese medical pathodynamics.

Chapter Three: Pathogenic Progression: Levels and Channels

So far, we've explored the history and etiology of Lingering Pathogenic Illness (LPI). Now it's time to turn our attention to its pathomechanisms. In this chapter, we'll examine the possible locations and trajectories of LPI, beginning with the Four Levels, moving through the Six Channel conformations, and concluding with the Membrane Source.

The Concept of Depth in Chinese Medicine

In Chinese medicine, the idea that illness can sink deeper into the body is not a metaphor; it is foundational. Ancient clinicians observed that some diseases pass through the system swiftly, only breaching the outermost channels, while other illnesses linger, becoming entrenched and harder to dislodge. These physicians developed layered frameworks to understand this phenomenon, each mapping how disease interacts with the body's structure and vitality. One of the most enduring of these frameworks is the concept of depth: that pathogenic influence begins at the exterior and, if unresolved, migrates inward through increasingly vital domains.

"Pathogenic Qi does not remain constant: when lodged in Yin, it flows into the viscera; when lodged in Yang, it flows into the channels."

-Huang Di Nei Jing Ling Shu[109]

[109] Text: Huang Di Nei Jing Ling Shu
Original: "邪气之中人也无有常，中于阴则溜于腑，中于阳则溜于经"

To speak of "depth" in Chinese medicine is to speak of trajectory. A pathogen begins as a superficial disruption, perhaps a "wind-cold invasion"[110] causing chills and fever, but if the patient lacks the strength to expel it, it may settle in the Qi level[111], stagnating movement, heating up, and consuming resources like Qi and Yin. Left unresolved, it may descend further, disturbing the Nutritive and Blood levels, or even burrow into the membrane source, an interstitial zone between organs and systems where chronic illness often hides.

Patients with unresolved febrile illnesses developed complex, evolving symptom patterns that could not be explained by surface-level patterns alone. Classical physicians like Ye Tianshi recognized that even when initial symptoms subsided, the illness itself often remained, manifesting as low-grade fever, fatigue, palpitations, insomnia, or unseasonal sweating.[112] Disease that was no longer acutely "visible" had gone underground, hijacking the body's terrain, and disguised itself within the body.

Contemporary medicine echoes this model in its own language. What Chinese physicians once called lurking heat or residual evil, we now describe as persistent immune activation, immune exhaustion, immune dysregulation, and autoimmunity. Conditions like ME, Long Covid, and chronic Lyme illustrate how disease can become systemic, not necessarily because the initial pathogen remains active, but because it has irreversibly altered the immune terrain. The result is not just inflammation, but the failure of resolution, an injury to the immune system's capacity for clearance and resolve.

Translation: "Pathogenic qi does not remain constant: when lodged in Yīn, it flows into the viscera; when lodged in Yáng, it flows into the channels."

[110] Wind Cold Invasion: A classical Chinese medicine pattern describing the early stage of an external illness caused by pathogenic wind and cold entering the body's surface. Symptoms typically include chills, mild fever, headache, stiff neck, clear nasal discharge, and absence of sweating, with a floating and tight pulse. It reflects the Wei (defensive) Qi's struggle against external cold at the body's surface and is often treated by gently releasing the exterior and warming the channels.

[111] Qi Level (Four Levels): The stage where the pathogen has moved deeper into the interior, often manifesting as high fever, profuse sweating, thirst, irritability, cough with yellow sputum, and a full, rapid pulse. This level corresponds to excess heat in the Yang organs, especially the Lungs, Stomach, and Intestines.

[112] Text: *Wēn Rè Lùn* (溫熱論), Discussion of Post-Heat Injury
Attributed Authors: Ye Tianshi (葉天士, 1666–1745)
Original (Ye Tianshi): "熱退之後，汗自出，神疲乏力。"
Translation: "After the heat recedes, spontaneous sweating and fatigue of the spirit appear."

In this chapter, we will explore the progression of lingering illness through the lens of the Four Levels (Wei, Qi, Ying, Blood) and the Channel System. These are dynamic frameworks that help us understand how pathogens behave in time and space, how symptoms shift, and how treatment must adapt. They show us why one patient develops brain fog while another is wracked with chest oppression, why one relapses seasonally, and another declines slowly over many years.

Understanding this progression is key to recognizing what Lingering Pathogenic Illness really is: not a single entity, but a unique trajectory, a chronic, patterned unfolding of disease through the body's energetic and immunological architecture.

The Four Levels (Wei, Qi, Ying, Blood)

The Four Levels theory, first articulated by Ye Tianshi during the Qing dynasty, was developed to map the progression of warm diseases, febrile illnesses that often entered through the nose and mouth and wreaked systemic havoc. Though it emerged in response to acute epidemics, the model is deeply relevant to Lingering Pathogenic Illness today. It offers a framework for understanding how pathogens traverse the body's layers, and what happens when the immune system fails to fully clear them.

Each level represents both a phase of disease progression and a domain of bodily function. The deeper the level, the more entrenched the pathology becomes. But importantly, this model reveals how a pathogen can become stuck, cycle between levels, or smolder at a particular depth.

Wei (Defensive Level)

The Wei level[113] corresponds to the body's outermost defenses, analogous to the skin and body hair, mucosal barriers, innate immunity, and even behavior like sweating or shivering. This is where most acute illnesses begin. Symptoms here include chills

[113] Wei Level (Four Levels): The defensive or most superficial layer of the body's response to warm pathogens. Symptoms include fever, slight chills, headache, sore throat, cough, thirst, and a floating, rapid pulse. This stage reflects early, external invasion where Wei Qi (defensive Qi) is battling the pathogen on the surface.

with aversion to cold, mild fever, sneezing, nasal congestion, slight thirst, and a red-tipped tongue with a floating pulse.

In the context of lingering illness, an unresolved Wei-level invasion might not cause intense symptoms, but it subtly weakens the surface defenses. This can manifest as seasonal allergies, sensitivity to wind or drafts, sweating disorders (inappropriate sweating or lack of sweating), or recurrent minor infections. The immune system may be stuck in a low-grade state of activation, never quite clearing, never quite resolving.

Qi Level

When a pathogen penetrates past the Wei level, it enters the Qi level, where it begins to interact with the body's metabolic and organ systems. This is the realm of active inflammation, characterized by fever, aversion to heat, sweating, cough, thirst, irritability, and a dry tongue coat with a slippery pulse. The immune system is now fully engaged in battle.

In lingering illness, this level often becomes a site of chronic immune dysregulation. Patients may experience inflammatory fatigue, heat flares, or digestive hypersensitivity. The Qi level also includes the Shaoyang channel, a half-interior, half-exterior domain where pathogens can get stuck in a kind of limbo. This is a critical stage in many post-viral syndromes, where the body continues to expend energy in a "holding pattern" without effective resolution.

Ying (Nutritive Level)

The Ying level is more interior and subtle, corresponding to the blood circulation and the central nervous system. In classical texts, symptoms here include fever that worsens at night, thirst with no desire to drink, restlessness, insomnia, mental confusion, confused speech, and faint maculopapular rashes.[114] This level marks the transition from inflammation to tissue damage and neuroinflammatory stress.

---

[114] Text: *Wēn Bìng Tiáo Biàn* (溫病條辨)
Section: Differentiation of Ying-Level Disorders (辨營分證)
Attributed Author: Wu Jutong (吳鞠通, 1758–1836)

For modern patients, this often appears as brain fog, autonomic instability, neuropathic pain, and sleep disorders. The immune system is now dysregulated in a way that affects cognition, mood, and regulatory function. Ying level injury may also involve mitochondrial damage and nutrient transport dysfunction, particularly where damp-heat obstructs the Spleen or Liver networks.

Blood Level

The Blood level is the deepest and most severe stage. Here, the pathogen has entered the very medium of life, causing systemic inflammation, coagulation issues, autoimmune activity, and potentially organ injury. Classical symptoms include fever, restlessness, bleeding(nosebleed, blood in stools), maculopapular rashes, and a deep red tongue.

In the context of lingering illness, this may manifest as dysautonomia, autoimmune dysregulation, blood stasis, or vascular inflammation. The patient may show signs of Yin deficiency, or conversely, smoldering heat trapped in the Blood layer that resurfaces cyclically, often during hormonal shifts or seasonal change.

Blood-level illness is particularly challenging to treat because it involves not just active inflammation, but failure of resolution, immune exhaustion, and autoimmune-like processes. The disease has become endogenous internally. The body, in trying to clear the original insult, begins to injure itself.

The Four Levels map a trajectory, but more than that, they offer insight into where a pathogen is lodged and how the body is reacting. In clinical practice, this helps guide both diagnosis and treatment: *do we need to release the exterior, harmonize Shaoyang, nourish the Ying, or cool the Blood?*

The Six Channels: Movement and Containment

Original: "營分證，其證夜熱早涼，舌絳而乾，神煩少寐，或時譫語。"
Translation: "Ying-level disorders present with fever worse at night, crimson dry tongue, agitation with little sleep, or occasional delirious speech."

If the Four Levels describe the depth of a pathogen's residence, the channel system describes its trajectory, how it enters, circulates, hides, and recurs. The twelve primary channels, along with their divisions into six conformations, provide a spatial and functional map for understanding disease movement. In the case of Lingering Pathogenic Illness, it is often not the depth alone but the misrouting and entrapment within specific channel systems that explain the complex, shifting symptoms.

Movement of Disease Through Channels

The disease often begins in the Taiyang (Bladder[115]/Small Intestine[116]) layer, the body's outermost defense, analogous to the Wei Qi level. If resolved quickly, it is expelled with minimal disruption. But if the Wei Qi is weak or overwhelmed, the pathogen may move inward or laterally into adjacent channels, initially Shaoyang (San Jiao[117]/Gallbladder[118]), or Yang Ming (Stomach[119]/Large Intestine[120]), each with its own implications. Note that some of the channels have overlapping symptoms.

❖ Taiyang (Bladder/Small Intestine): chronic dysfunction can result in chronic tightness of the occiput and neck, a floating pulse[121], cold sensitivity, generalized

---

[115] Urinary Bladder(TCM/organ/channel): Stores and excretes urine; paired with the Kidney. Its channel passes through the back and connects with the brain. Often implicated in pain, tension, fluid imbalance, and post-viral dysautonomia.

[116] Small Intestine(TCM/organ/channel): Separates the clear from the turbid, both physically and mentally. Imbalances may involve digestive issues, fever, or urinary dysfunction. Paired with the Heart, it reflects clarity in both digestion and discernment.

[117] San Jiao(TCM/organ/channel): The Triple Burner or Triple Heater, responsible for coordinating water and Qi movement across the body's three burners (upper, middle, lower). Often interpreted as a regulatory or metabolic network rather than a physical organ.

[118] Gallbladder(TCM/organ/channel): Associated with decision-making, courage, and the flow of bile in digestion. The Gallbladder channel is also key to Shaoyang dynamics and is often involved in conditions with alternation, constraint, or Dampness and Heat.

[119] Stomach(TCM/organ/channel): Controls receiving and ripening of food and fluids. Its harmony is essential for postnatal Qi production. Often involved in Damp-Heat, phlegm accumulation, and digestion-related manifestations of LPI.

[120] Large Intestine(TCM/organ/channel): Responsible for eliminating waste and maintaining bowel function. Paired with the Lung, it reflects the balance between intake and release. Frequently involved in Damp-Heat patterns, dysbiosis, and post-infectious bowel issues.

[121] Floating Pulse (Fú Mài):A pulse that is most distinct with light pressure and weakens or disappears with deeper palpation. Traditionally associated with external invasions (e.g., Wind-Cold or Wind-Heat), it may also indicate deficiency at the surface, such as Wei Qi or Blood deficiency. In Lingering Pathogenic Illness, it can reflect unresolved

body pain, clammy or even itchy skin. Patients may present with a vulnerability to wind and cold, heat effusion, symptoms that change with weather, persistent headaches, and congestion, hallmarks of an exterior vacuity that leave the patient vulnerable to invading pathogens and climatic factors.

- Shaoyang (San Jiao/Gallbladder): the pivot between interior and exterior, is often the site where pathogens become stuck, never fully expelled, never fully absorbed. This leads to alternating heat effusion and aversion to cold (heat when the Zheng Qi is prevailing, cold when the pathogen is prevailing), fatigue with disinclination to talk, no appetite or thirst, fullness in the chest and rib-side tension, dry and/or sore throat, bitter taste in the mouth, irritability, dizzy vision, nausea, headaches, and a fine, string-like pulse.
- Yangming (Stomach/Large Intestine): represents a gastrointestinal but still active exterior layer. In unresolved illness, this can manifest as gut inflammation, acid regurgitation, heat effusion with aversion to heat, possible tidal fever, unquenchable thirst, food intolerance, gnawing hunger and/or nausea, muscle heaviness, spontaneous sweating, constipation, and a large pulse.
- Taiyin (Spleen/Lung): is the channel of nourishment and Dampness. Chronic fatigue, abdominal fullness and pain, vomiting, muscle aches, spontaneous sweating, shortness of breath, and severe diarrhea or phlegmy stools (sticky/loose/irregular) often arise from Dampness or Cold retention in Taiyin due to Spleen deficiency. It's also the most easily injured layer during or after illness, especially in post-viral fatigue and post-exertional crashes (most people are somewhat Spleen/Lung Qi deficient). Damp encumbrance due to Spleen deficiency stifles function throughout the body, eventually affecting the Kidney Qi and Yang as well.
- Shaoyin (Heart/Kidney): represents the innermost fire-water axis, the regulation of spirit, will, and life force. Lingering pathogens that penetrate this deep can cause symptoms such as palpitations, insomnia, low back weakness, achy/swollen joints, frequent urination, thirst, diarrhea, Heart vexation, anxiety, and fatigue with a strong desire to sleep. These are among the most complex and intractable cases of LPI, where exhaustion coexists with either Cold or Heat

pathogens near the exterior or a weakened ability to regulate surface defenses. Interpretation depends on context and accompanying pulse qualities.

signs, and where tonification can backfire without first unblocking and regulating the Heart and Kidney axis.

- Jueyin (Liver/Pericardium[122]): controls the return current of blood and Qi and the deepest regulation of blood and temperature. Dysfunction here is marked by heat above and cold below, intractable hunger and thirst with inability to eat and vomiting, hiccups, persistent diarrhea, neurovascular instability, muscle spasms/tremors, frequent urination, and cold legs and feet. In modern terms, this maps closely with more advanced stages of ME.

The Channels as Containers

The six channels aren't just highways; they're containment systems. When functioning, they guide and isolate pathogenic influences. But when weakened or overwhelmed, pathogens leak out of containment, settling into extraordinary vessels[123], membrane source, or even the collaterals[124], which then store latent heat, dampness, and blood stasis. In a lingering illness, this can look like:

- Fluctuating symptoms that change location and form.
- Organ systems affected in an inexplicable sequence.
- Disjointed labs with no clear pathology.
- Treatment responses that are inconsistent or temporary.

---

[122] Pericardium: The Heart's protector in Chinese medicine, responsible for shielding the Heart from heat pathogens and regulating emotional and Shen (spirit) activity. It plays a key role in febrile and emotional disorders, especially when heat reaches the Ying level and disturbs consciousness.

[123] Extraordinary Vessels: Eight ancestral channels that regulate, integrate, and buffer the functions of the primary meridians. The Extraordinary Vessels act as reservoirs of Qi and Blood, governing inherited constitution, reproductive cycles, psycho-emotional integration, and the body's response to trauma or deep constitutional shifts. Unlike the twelve regular meridians, they do not correspond to Zang-Fu organs directly, but instead reflect pre-natal influence (Jing), ancestral memory, and adaptive resilience. In clinical practice, they are often activated in complex, systemic, or treatment-resistant conditions—especially those involving hormonal regulation, chronic inflammation, or layered trauma.

[124] Collaterals: The branching vessels that extend from the primary channels to reach the body's surface, interior, and finer structures. Collaterals are the network of smaller channels that distribute Qi and Blood beyond the main meridians, ensuring communication between organs, tissues, and sensory or emotional pathways. They regulate circulation in areas not directly governed by the twelve regular meridians and play a key role in local symptoms, hidden pathogens, and chronic stagnation. Pathology in the collaterals often presents as tingling, numbness, fixed pain, or lingering heat. In warm disease theory and chronic illness, they are especially important when pathogens bypass the regular channels to embed deeper or more diffusely.

The exhaustion of the Taiyin-Shaoyin-Jueyin axis, in particular, often corresponds with the post-exertional malaise, gut-brain dysfunction, and loss of constitutional resilience we see in ME and Long Covid. This represents not just a pattern of deficiency, but a failure of movement, communication, and containment across the channels.

Membrane Source and Hidden Pathogens

Among the most elusive concepts in Chinese medicine is the membrane source, or *mo yuan*. Classically described in the *Shang Han Lun* and expanded upon by later physicians, the membrane source is understood to be a liminal space, neither organ nor exterior, not entirely Blood nor Qi.[125] It is the terrain between, a moist, protective field of connective tissue and interstitial flow where lingering pathogens often hide.

The *mo yuan* is not a fixed anatomical structure. In theory, it overlaps functionally with the mesentery, interfascial planes, peritoneum, and glymphatic and interstitial fluid systems. More symbolically, it is the interface where systems meet, the invisible architecture between organs, channels, and fluids. When a pathogen cannot be expelled, fully absorbed, or destroyed, the body may quarantine it in this space. It becomes wrapped in dampness or biofilm, obscured from direct immune surveillance.

Later physicians described this as "hidden heat in the membrane source." These are illnesses without surface signs but with unmistakable internal disturbance: persistent low-grade fever, fullness in the chest or epigastrium, bitter taste, emotional volatility, and fatigue that defies classification. Formulas like Da Yuan Yin[126] were

---

[125] Text: *Shāng Hán Lùn* (傷寒論); Expanded in *Wēn Rè Lùn* (溫熱論)
Attributed Authors: Zhang Zhongjing (張仲景, ca. 150–219 CE); Ye Tianshi (葉天士, 1666–1745)
Commentary (Ye Tianshi): "膜原者，非臟腑之內，非經絡之外。"
Translation: "The membrane source is neither within the organs nor outside the channels."

[126] Da Yuan Yin: Translated as "Reach the Source Decoction," Da Yuan Yin was first recorded by Wu Youke in the *Wen Yi Lun* (Treatise on Epidemic Febrile Disease, 1642) as a treatment for epidemic pathogens trapped in the membrane source (**膜原**, *mo yuan*), the interstitial space between the diaphragm and the middle burner. The formula combines Hou Po, Cao Guo, Bing Lang, Zhi Mu, Huang Qin, Bai Shao, and Gan Cao to release constraint at this level, transform damp-turbidity, clear heat, and harmonize the Shaoyang. Classically it was indicated for alternating fever and chills, chest and hypochondriac fullness, nausea, thirst with inability to drink, and a greasy yellow tongue coat. In modern practice, Da Yuan Yin and its variations are used to address Lingering Pathogenic Illness and post-viral syndromes, including Long Covid, where pathogens remain hidden in "in-between" spaces, producing cyclical symptoms such as digestive upset, neurological complaints, and alternating hot and cold sensations. Contemporary

designed specifically to mobilize and expel these hidden pathogens, pushing them back toward the surface where they could be cleared.[127]

Why the Pathogen Disappears from View

The membrane source becomes critical in Lingering Pathogenic Illness because it explains why diagnostic tests often show nothing, and why symptoms don't follow organ-specific patterns. The immune system knows something is wrong, but cannot mount an effective response. The pathogen is not gone; it is displaced, fragmented, obscured, outside circulation. And in its hiding, it continues to influence the system.

This is where many modern patients, especially those with ME, Long Covid, or chronic Lyme, get dismissed. Conventional labs return within normal ranges. Conventional inflammatory markers are mild or absent. Yet symptoms persist, evolve, and intensify. The patient becomes a diagnostic paradox, difficult to diagnose with conventional testing, but clearly very unwell.

In Chinese medicine, this paradox is not mysterious. The presence of Heat, Dampness, and Phlegm; the relapsing fevers (subjective and objective); the stasis that manifests emotionally, neurologically, and physically - these all point to membrane source pathology.

When Progression is Not Linear

The classical Chinese medical model presents a clear trajectory of pathogenic progression, external evils penetrate from the surface inward, through the Wei, Qi,

---

modifications, such as Qing Pi Tang, adapt the formula to strengthen Spleen Qi, clear residual heat, and calm the Shen. From a biomedical perspective, its actions may be understood as modulating immune dysregulation at barrier sites such as the gut–lung axis, where persistent pathogens and inflammatory mediators create cycles of inflammation and exhaustion.

[127] Text: *Jīn Guì Yào Lüè* (金匱要略), Gui Zhi jia Huang Qi Tang; *Wēn Yì Lùn* (瘟疫論), Da Yuan Yin
Attributed Authors: Zhang Zhongjing (張仲景, ca. 150–219 CE); Wu Youke (吳又可, 1582–1652)
Original (Gui Zhi jia Huang Qi Tang): "發汗後，身體腫，脈浮大者，桂枝加黃芪湯主之。"
Translation: "After sweating, if the body becomes swollen and the pulse is floating and large, Gui Zhi jia Huang Qi Tang governs."
Original (Da Yuan Yin): "邪在膜原，氣口脈浮大者，可用大元飲宣解膜邪。"
Translation: "When the pathogen resides in the membrane source and the pulse is floating and large at the qi opening, Da Yuan Yin can be used to disperse and resolve membrane-bound pathogens."

Ying, and Blood levels, or along the six channels from Taiyang to Jueyin. In clinical practice, however, the path of Lingering Pathogenic Illness rarely conforms to these neat patterns. The movement of the pathogen is often recursive, cyclical, and unpredictable. It is shaped less by textbooks than by the patient's constitutional deficiencies, trauma, and the resilience or weakness of their channel systems.

Rather than a predictable descent from exterior to interior, lingering pathogens often seem to burrow erratically, shift positions, or hide for long periods before reappearing, sometimes violently. A patient may begin treatment with Blood-level symptoms like agitation, insomnia, or post-exertional malaise, only to develop Qi-level patterns of digestive inflammation, chest oppression, or subjective heat. Another patient might appear to improve for months before erupting with Wei-level symptoms such as rashes, sinus pressure, or allergic rhinitis.

These progressions do not necessarily indicate treatment failure or regression. Rather, the practitioner should remind the patient that changes in immunopathology are a natural part of a Lingering Pathogenic Illness being dislodged from its depths.

As Liu Bao-Yi wrote, "Lurking warm pathogens have many layers. After resolution and a cessation, one may proceed to evict through the next layer. Moreover, the pathogen of subsequent layers will invariably be more fixed than the first."[128] His observation rings true in cases where apparent healing gives way to a new set of symptoms while a pathogen is still stuck in the deeper Taiyin-Shaoyin-Jueyin systems. It may seem like regression, but it's not. Each stage of resolution lifts the veil on the next. As the body reasserts immune control, the pathogen is forced to exit through the terrain it once occupied, often through the patient's weakest or most vulnerable pathways (the last pathways to fully benefit from treatment in terms of recovery).

Lei Shou-Yi described this process succinctly: "The outward expression of lingering pathogens must follow the weak spots in channel Qi: there is no certain route out of

[128] Text: *Wēn Rè Fēng Yuán* (溫熱逢原)
Section: Treatise on Lingering Warm Pathogens (論伏溫邪)
Attributed Author: Liu Bao-Yi (劉保儀, 1842–1901)
Original: "伏溫之邪，層層深入，層層解去，然後為愈。每層之邪，較前一層更甚。"
Translation: "Lurking warm pathogens have many layers. Only by resolving each layer in sequence can healing occur. The pathogen in each subsequent layer is more fixed than the last."

the body."[129] Clinically, this means that the body does not adhere to our desired treatment sequence. Pathology exits where it can, not necessarily where we want it to. That movement may be lateral, vertical, or circuitous.

It also requires care in the herbal strategy. When a patient becomes febrile or inflamed during a course of immune and Qi tonics, it may be tempting to suppress with cold or heavy herbs. But Liu Bao-Yi reminds us: "Although it's inappropriate to use pungent and warm dispersing methods, one should also avoid using cold herbs that hinder the pathogen's outward movement."[130] In other words, treatments must balance support and release, stabilizing without trapping, facilitating resolve without exhausting.

In Lingering Pathogenic Illness, healing is rarely linear. Symptoms can resurface or appear to regress even as the immune system becomes more competent. But if we track the movement, not just the noise, we begin to see the spiral unfold. Not a descent into confusion, but a cyclical return toward resolution.

---

[129] Text: *Clinical Handbook of Internal Medicine, Volume 3: Qi Blood Fluid Channels*
Attributed Author: Lei Shou-Yi (雷守儀), as cited in Maclean, William; Lyttleton, Jane; Bayley, Mark; Taylor, Kathryn
Edition: 3rd Volume, 1st Edition
Publisher: Eastland Press, 2010
Quotation (as cited): "The outward expression of lingering pathogen must follow the weak spots in channel qi; there is no fixed route out of the body."
Note: This quote is attributed to Lei Shou-Yi in the context of lingering pathogens but may be a paraphrase or lineage transmission. The original source text is not explicitly cited.

[130] Text: *Wēn Rè Fēng Yuán* (溫熱逢原)
Section: Discussion of Treatment Principles for Residual Pathogens (論治伏邪)
Attributed Author: Liu Bao-Yi (劉保儀, 1842–1901)
Original: "不可用辛熱之劑，發散太過；亦不可用寒涼之藥，阻其外達。"
Translation: "Although it's inappropriate to use pungent and warm dispersing methods, one should also avoid using cold herbs that hinder the pathogen's outward movement."

Chapter 4: Immune Injury: APC Dysfunction and FcγR Pathology

Let's shift gears, from a classical Chinese perspective on Lingering Pathogenic Illness (LPI) to a modern biomedical lens. In this chapter, we'll consider the possible pathomechanisms underlying LPI from an immunological and systems biology standpoint. I'll close by introducing a mnemonic that I've found useful in thinking about complex chronic illness: PM VEINS.

Lingering Pathogenic Illness may not be explained solely by the persistence of a pathogen. Increasingly, it appears to involve immune injury that leaves the host unable to fully clear non-self or restore immune equilibrium. One possible mechanism at the heart of this breakdown is dysfunction in antigen-presenting cells (APCs), the cells at the critical interface between innate detection and adaptive precision. When this interface is impaired, both immune recognition and immune tolerance are likely to falter.[131]

The initial injury in LPI, regardless of cause (see Chapter 2), creates the downstream patterns of Qi and Yin deficiency. While some individuals may enter illness with these deficits,[132] Qi and Yin deficiency are usually the consequence of unresolved immune trauma and persistent inflammation.

---

[131] Juedes, A. E., & von Herrath, M. G. (2003). "Using regulatory APCs to induce/maintain tolerance." *Annals of the New York Academy of Sciences*, 1005, 128–137. https://doi.org/10.1196/annals.1288.014

[132] Georgopoulos AP, James LM, Peterson PK. "Human Leukocyte Antigen (HLA) at the Root of Persistent Antigens and Long COVID." *J Immunol Sci.* 2025 Jan 6;9(1):1-3. doi: 10.29245/2578-3009/2025/1.1257. PMID: 39949480; PMCID: PMC11823424.

My focus on antigen-presenting cells (APCs) emerged while I was narrowing down herbs for use in Lingering Pathogenic Illness. Guided by Liu Bao-Yi, I selected herbs that emphasized tonifying Qi and Yin, venting residual heat, and draining fluids. As I compared these herbs, a pattern became apparent: many of the core medicinals in such formulas appear to support antigen-presenting cell function (these herbs and their functions are listed in Chapter 6). By contrast, the harsh purgatives and extreme cold or hot herbs, discouraged by Liu Bao-Yi, often demonstrated immunosuppressive effects, which may help explain their exclusion from LPI protocols. This observation, together with clinical outcomes and modern research, has shaped my working hypothesis about the role of APCs in LPI theory. Before exploring this further, let's first consider what it means for antigen-presenting cells to be dysfunctional in Lingering Pathogenic Illness.

APC Dysfunction and the Loss of Immunologic Clarity

In both immunology and Chinese medicine, we encounter the same paradox: a system that is inflamed and dysfunctional at once. Nowhere is this duality more evident than in the dysfunction of antigen-presenting cells (APCs) such as dendritic cells, monocytes, and macrophages. These are the cells that detect pathogens, initiate responses, and orchestrate resolution. In the wake of SARS-CoV-2 infection, especially in those who develop Long Covid, this network falters.[133]

Rather than simply being suppressed by inhibitory signaling (covered in part in the next section), subsets of APCs are depleted and erratic in a myriad of ways.[134][135] In Long Covid and related chronic syndromes, B cell compartments are both depleted and disorganized.[136] Importantly, regulatory B cells (Bregs), which preserve tolerance, are also reduced, and the loss of Bregs in Long Covid correlates strongly

---

[133] Chang, T., Yang, J., Deng, H., Chen, D., Yang, X., & Tang, Z.-H. (2022). "Depletion and dysfunction of dendritic cells: Understanding SARS-CoV-2 infection." *Frontiers in Immunology*, **13**, 843342. https://doi.org/10.3389/fimmu.2022.843342

[134] Klein, J., Wood, J., Jaycox, J.R. *et al.* "Distinguishing features of long COVID identified through immune profiling." *Nature* 623, 139–148 (2023). https://doi.org/10.1038/s41586-023-06651-y

[135] Pasharawipas, T. (2025). "Perspective: Host factor variants and the underlying causes of Long COVID." *Frontiers in Medicine*, 12, 1603317. https://doi.org/10.3389/fmed.2025.1603317

[136] Noviello, M., Manfredi, M., Bongiovanni, D., et al. (2024). "The longitudinal characterization of immune responses in COVID-19 patients reveals novel prognostic signatures for disease severity, patients' survival and Long COVID." *Frontiers in Immunology*, 15, 1381091. https://doi.org/10.3389/fimmu.2024.1381091

with persistent symptoms. Meanwhile, these APCs shift their metabolism toward anaerobic glycolysis[137], an emergency, short-term adaptation that becomes damaging when prolonged. The result is a breakdown in phagocytosis[138], autophagy[139], and immune communication. These cells do not clear danger; they restrain it very poorly, and the whole body suffers.

This environment in Lingering Pathogenic Illness, characterized by unresolved antigens and dysregulated signaling, feeds a vicious cycle. Incompletely processed immune complexes continue to stimulate immune cells, triggering low-grade inflammation and functional exhaustion.[140] Instead of resolving the initial threat, the immune system becomes trapped in a state of confusion and congestion, unable to resolve.

In chronic viral syndromes, including ME/CFS and Long Covid, we see the imprint of this immune dysfunction.[141] Plasmacytoid dendritic cells are often depleted. Interferon signaling lingers long past the initial threat.[142] Inflammatory monocytes dominate but lack the function to clear or organize.[143] Chinese medicine has long

---

[137] Anaerobic Glycolysis: A metabolic pathway that allows cells to generate energy (ATP) by breaking down glucose in the absence of oxygen. Instead of proceeding through the full mitochondrial oxidative cycle, glucose is converted to lactate - yielding rapid but inefficient energy production. While essential during acute stress or hypoxia, chronic reliance on anaerobic glycolysis reflects metabolic dysfunction, as seen in immune exhaustion, cancer, and persistent viral syndromes. It promotes acidosis, inflammation, and cellular fatigue. In TCM, this state resembles Qi Stagnation with Damp or Phlegm, where the system is forced to rely on short-term, inefficient energy, ultimately leading to depletion of Zheng Qi and accumulation of turbid byproducts.

[138] Phagocytosis: The process by which immune cells such as macrophages or dendritic cells engulf and digest cellular debris, pathogens, or immune complexes. Failure of this mechanism can lead to inflammation, autoimmunity, or persistent infection.

[139] Autophagy: A cellular housekeeping process in which cells degrade and recycle their own damaged components, including misfolded proteins, dysfunctional organelles, and intracellular pathogens. Autophagy supports cellular health, regulates immune responses, and plays a critical role in maintaining metabolic balance. Dysregulation of autophagy is implicated in chronic infections, immune exhaustion, and neuroinflammatory conditions.

[140] Edwards, J., Cambridge, G., & Cliff, J. M. (2025). "A proposed mechanism for ME/CFS invoking macrophage FcγRI and interferon gamma." Preprint, Qeios. https://doi.org/10.32388/8GI3CT

[141] Sun, Y., Zhang, Z., Qiao, Q. *et al.* "Immunometabolic changes and potential biomarkers in CFS peripheral immune cells revealed by single-cell RNA sequencing." *J Transl Med* 22, 925 (2024). https://doi.org/10.1186/s12967-024-05710-w

[142] Krishna, B. A., Lim, E. Y., Metaxaki, M., Jackson, S., Mactavous, L., Lyons, P. A., Doffinger, R., Bradley, J. R., Smith, K. G. C., Sinclair, J., Matheson, N. J., Lehner, P. J., Sithole, N., & Wills, M. R. (2024). "Spontaneous, persistent, T cell–dependent IFN-γ release in patients who progress to Long COVID." *Science Advances*, 10(7), eadi9379. https://doi.org/10.1126/sciadv.adi9379
(Nadirs in IFN signaling also occur in Long Covid patients.)

[143] Singh, R., Hemati, H., Bajpai, M., Yadav, P., Maheshwari, A., Kumar, S., Agrawal, S., Sevak, J. K., Islam, M., Mars, J. S., Sarin, S. K., & Trehanpati, N. (2021). "Sustained expression of inflammatory monocytes and activated T

observed this state, including pathogens that persist, illnesses that relapse seasonally, pulses that are faint and wiry, and tongues that are pale with red tips or edges. These diagnostics indicate a loss of function and vitality with persistent toxicity and inflammation.

This perspective suggests that the treatment of Lingering Pathogenic Illness may need to go beyond purely anti-inflammatory or antiviral approaches, which can sometimes worsen underlying deficiency. Effective care appears to be more reconstructive, supporting antigen presentation, restoring resolution pathways, and strengthening the body's ability to distinguish self from non-self. In formulating herbal treatments, this means carefully balancing stimulation and nourishment with clearing and draining.

My favorite analogy for this and the following concept is Roadrunner and Wile E. Coyote. In this analogy, Roadrunner represents a persistent antigen or the build-up of immune complexes, while Wile E. Coyote represents immune cells that have lost both antigenic and tolerogenic tone. The more effort, wit, and ammunition Wile E. Coyote uses to catch Roadrunner, the greater his attacks backfire. This imagery captures the fate of the immune system when it tries to react to non-self in Lingering Pathogenic Illnesses: unproductive and self-destructive. In the following section, we will go over this form of poorly controlled hyperreactivity. (Fun fact: the E. in Wile E. Coyote stands for "Ethelburt.")

Persistent Fc Gamma Receptor Pathology and "APC Exhaustion"

If antigen-presenting cell injury is the initiating wound in Lingering Pathogenic Illness, then Fc gamma receptor (FcγR) pathology is the chronic irritant that keeps the wound open. These receptors, expressed on immune cells like monocytes, macrophages, neutrophils, and dendritic cells, bind to the Fc (fragment crystallizable) region of IgG antibodies (on immune complexes) and play a vital role in immune complex clearance, phagocytosis, and cytokine regulation. In normal physiology, FcγRs act as mediators between immune surveillance and immune restraint. But in the setting of unresolved infection or antigen persistence, they

---

cells in COVID-19 patients and recovered convalescent plasma donors." *Immunity, Inflammation and Disease*, 9(4), 1396–1407. https://doi.org/10.1002/iid3.476

become chronically engaged in a way that misguides the immune system into perpetual irritation.[144]

Persistent antigens, whether viral debris, fungal fragments, or incompletely phagocytosed material, lead to an overload of immune complexes that bind to activating FcγRs. These receptors respond by triggering ongoing low-grade inflammatory cascades. Over time, this chronic stimulation fuels the release of proinflammatory cytokines like IL-6 and TNF-α, which, I believe, in part, contribute to the neuroinflammation, vascular injury, and mitochondrial suppression seen in LPI.

This pathological loop does more than maintain inflammation; it distorts immune recognition. Chronic FcγR engagement appears to suppress APC signaling further, disrupting antigen processing, reducing HLA-DR[145] expression, and contributing to the broader dysfunction in immune coherence seen in post-viral fatigue syndromes. It is not simply that inflammation persists, but that resolution fails, and the cycle continues.

Fc gamma receptors include inhibitory subtypes like FcγRIIb[146], which normally dampen the immune response once a threat has been cleared. In chronic infections, this inhibitory signaling, meant to quell aberrant immune activity, becomes erratic, further reducing clearance by APCs and contributing to symptoms. This imbalance ultimately overwhelms the immune system, so even low-level exposures, such as mold, food particles, or stress, can trigger disproportionate immune responses. With fluctuations in APC function and inhibitory tone, minor inputs (or outputs like exertion[147]) can provoke major flare-ups, as seen in Long Covid and ME/CFS.

---

[144] Yamada, D. H., Elsaesser, H., Lux, A., Timmerman, J. M., Morrison, S. L., de la Torre, J. C., Nimmerjahn, F., & Brooks, D. G. (2015). "Suppression of Fcγ-receptor-mediated antibody effector function during persistent viral infection." *Immunity*, 42(2), 379–390. 10.1016/j.immuni.2015.01.005

[145] HLA-DR (Human Leukocyte Antigen - DR Isotype): A major histocompatibility complex (MHC) class II molecule found on the surface of antigen-presenting cells. It presents extracellular antigens to CD4+ T cells, initiating adaptive immune responses. Reduced or absent HLA-DR expression on monocytes is a biomarker of immune paralysis or antigen-presenting cell dysfunction in sepsis, post-viral syndromes, and chronic inflammatory conditions.

[146] FcγRIIb (Fc Gamma Receptor IIb): The only known inhibitory Fc gamma receptor, expressed primarily on B cells and antigen-presenting cells. It helps downregulate immune activation by modulating antibody signaling. Impaired FcγRIIb function can lead to unrestrained inflammation and autoimmunity. Its dysfunction may be central to exaggerated immune responses in ME/CFS and Long Covid.

[147] Van Booven, D. J., Gamer, J., Joseph, A., Perez, M., Zarnowski, O., Pandya, M., Collado, F., Klimas, N., Oltra, E., & Nathanson, L. (2023). "Stress-induced transcriptomic changes in females with Myalgic Encephalomyelitis/Chronic Fatigue Syndrome reveal disrupted immune signatures." *International Journal of*

This is, in part, why immunosuppressants often fail in treating LPI. While they may temporarily dampen symptoms, they also impair the very systems (APCs, etc.) needed for immune recognition. What's needed is not suppression but a nuanced clinical approach: supporting antigen clearance, restoring regulatory function, and carefully balancing immune tone.

FcγR pathology may serve as a bridge between unresolved antigen and the lived experience of fatigue, flare, and dysfunction. This perspective helps explain why illness and even recovery can feel *cyclical, discouraging, and uncomfortable*. When considered alongside APC dysfunction, it suggests a framework for understanding Lingering Pathogenic Illness not simply as a residual state, but as a possible ongoing failure of immune discrimination and repair./

IDO Hyperactivation[148] and Tryptophan Depletion

Chronic interferon signaling and Fcγ receptor engagement can induce sustained IDO expression in dendritic cells and monocytes.[149] This leads to depletion of tryptophan and accumulation of immunosuppressive kynurenines, which promote tolerogenic APC phenotypes, impair antigen presentation, and contribute to immune exhaustion. IDO-driven tryptophan catabolism may act as a key axis in APC depletion and dysfunction in Long Covid and related post-viral syndromes.[150] In essence, this is metabolic immune burnout. APCs lose their command.

Molecular Sciences, 24(3), 2698. https://doi.org/10.3390/ijms24032698
(This study found that exertion in patients with ME/CFS impairs immune cell subsets including APCs)

[148] IDO Hyperactivation: The pathological overexpression of the enzyme indoleamine 2,3-dioxygenase (IDO), often triggered by chronic immune stimulation such as interferon-γ signaling. IDO breaks down tryptophan into kynurenine and other metabolites that suppress immune function. When overactive, IDO promotes immune tolerance, inhibits antigen-presenting cells, and contributes to T cell exhaustion and chronic inflammation. It is implicated in Long Covid, ME/CFS, cancer, and persistent viral syndromes.

[149] Andrew L. Mellor, David H. Munn; "Tryptophan Catabolism and Regulation of Adaptive Immunity." *J Immunol* 15 June 2003; 170 (12): 5809–5813. https://doi.org/10.4049/jimmunol.170.12.5809

[150] Al-Hakeim, Hussein Kadhem, et al. "Tryptophan Catabolites, Inflammation, and Insulin Resistance as Determinants of Chronic Fatigue Syndrome and Affective Symptoms in Long Covid." *Frontiers*, Frontiers, 29 June 2025, www.frontiersin.org/journals/molecular-neuroscience/articles/10.3389/fnmol.2023.1194769/full.

Itaconate Shunt and Succinate Accumulation

Chronic innate immune activation, particularly through TLRs (toll-like receptors)[151] and sustained Fcγ receptor engagement, induces IRG1 (immune-responsive gene 1)[152] expression and reroutes citrate metabolism through the itaconate shunt. While initially anti-inflammatory, this shift disrupts mitochondrial metabolism by inhibiting succinate dehydrogenase (SDH)[153], leading to succinate accumulation and respiratory chain dysfunction. Elevated succinate stabilizes HIF-1α[154], driving IL-1β production and maintaining glycolytic, hypoxic, and pro-inflammatory immune states. In antigen-presenting cells (APCs), this metabolic detour undermines mitochondrial integrity, impairing energy-dependent processes like antigen processing, MHC expression, and costimulatory signaling. At the same time, succinate amplifies FcγR-mediated inflammation, potentiating mast cell degranulation, Th2 polarization, and oxidative stress. The result is a feedback loop in which APCs lose metabolic clarity and immunologic precision.

---

151 Toll-Like Receptor (TLR): A class of innate immune receptors that recognize molecular patterns from pathogens or damaged cells, initiating immune activation. TLRs trigger cytokine release and antigen-presenting cell maturation, serving as key gatekeepers between innate and adaptive immunity. In chronic illness, dysregulated TLR signaling may drive ongoing inflammation or immune tolerance. In Chinese medicine terms, TLRs reflect Wei Qi vigilance - too strong, they may generate internal Wind or Heat; too weak, they allow Lingering Pathogens to embed deeper into the system.

152 IRG-1 (Immune-Responsive Gene 1): A mitochondrial enzyme upregulated in innate immune cells during infection or inflammation. Its primary function is to catalyze the production of itaconate, a metabolite that modulates immunity by inhibiting succinate dehydrogenase (SDH) and dampening inflammatory signaling pathways. While itaconate helps resolve acute inflammation and prevent tissue damage, sustained IRG-1 activation can suppress mitochondrial function and impair antigen presentation. In chronic illness, this may contribute to immune tolerance, metabolic exhaustion, and APC dysfunction. In TCM terms, IRG-1 reflects the system's attempt to "cool Heat" and preserve Yin, but in excess may lead to Cold Phlegm, stagnation, and collapse of Zheng Qi.

153 Succinate Dehydrogenase (SDH): A key mitochondrial enzyme that functions at the intersection of the tricarboxylic acid (TCA) cycle and the electron transport chain (Complex II). SDH oxidizes succinate to fumarate, facilitating ATP production and maintaining metabolic flow. It also regulates intracellular succinate levels, which act as signaling molecules in inflammation. Inhibition of SDH - by metabolites like itaconate - leads to succinate accumulation, driving hypoxia-inducible factor (HIF-1α) stabilization, cytokine production (e.g. IL-1β), and inflammatory signaling. In chronic illness, impaired SDH activity contributes to immune dysfunction and metabolic stalling.

154 HIF-1α (Hypoxia-Inducible Factor 1-alpha) is a transcription factor that functions as a master regulator of cellular response to low oxygen (hypoxia). Under normal oxygen levels, HIF-1α is rapidly degraded; in hypoxic conditions, it stabilizes and translocates to the nucleus, where it dimerizes with HIF-1β to activate the transcription of genes involved in angiogenesis, glycolysis, erythropoiesis, and cell survival. While this mechanism is adaptive in acute stress, chronic stabilization of HIF-1α contributes to pathological states, including cancer, fibrosis, chronic inflammation, and immune dysregulation. In Lingering Pathogenic Illness, persistent activation of HIF-1α can drive metabolic reprogramming of immune cells, shifting them toward glycolysis and sustaining inflammatory signaling even in the absence of active infection. This creates a milieu of tissue hypoxia, mitochondrial dysfunction, and immune exhaustion that mirrors the patterns of hidden heat and Qi stagnation described in classical Chinese medicine.

PM VEINS: A Framework for Lingering Immune Injury

To help capture the complexity of LPI, I suggest the acronym PM VEINS, a mnemonic that organizes seven interlocking systems of dysfunction that appear to emerge after immune trauma.

P = Persistent Antigen

Residual antigen and/or fragments and immune debris (immune complexes) remain in tissues because APCs are unable to clear them efficiently.[155][156] This corresponds to classical Chinese medicine's concept of lurking heat or unresolved toxin in LPI.

M = Metabolic Reprogramming

Immune injury drives mitochondria into a defensive state, favoring persistent glycolysis over efficient respiration.[157] Energy production is restrained, lactate builds, and fatigue, PEM, and indigestion emerge. This mirrors a severe Spleen Qi deficiency pattern, a system stuck in urgency, unable to recover or restore.

---

[155] Zuo, W., He, D., Liang, C., Du, S., Hua, Z., Nie, Q., … & Zhan, Y. (2024). "The persistence of SARS-CoV-2 in tissues and its association with long COVID symptoms: A cross-sectional cohort study in China." *The Lancet Infectious Diseases*, 24(8), 845–855. https://doi.org/10.1016/S1473-3099(24)00171-3

[156] Chang, T., Yang, J., Deng, H., Chen, D., Yang, X., & Tang, Z.-H. (2022). Depletion and dysfunction of dendritic cells: Understanding SARS-CoV-2 infection. *Frontiers in Immunology*, 13, 843342. https://doi.org/10.3389/fimmu.2022.843342

[157] Naidu, A. S., Wang, C.-K., Rao, P., Mancini, F., Clemens, R. A., Wirakartakusumah, A., Chiu, H.-F., Yen, C.-H., Porretta, S., Mathai, I., & Naidu, S. A. G. (2024). "Precision nutrition to reset virus-induced human metabolic reprogramming and dysregulation (HMRD) in long-COVID." *NPJ Science of Food*, 8(1), Article 19.

V = Vascular Injury

Microvascular inflammation, hypercoagulability, and poor circulation limit oxygen delivery, echoing blood stasis and collateral vessel stagnation in classical Chinese medicine.[158][159]

E = Exhaustion (Immune)

Not just "low" immunity, this refers to cells that are functionally spent or depleted, with or without the additional production of inhibitory markers. In classical Chinese medicine, Zheng Qi is disoriented and depleted from prolonged engagement.

I = Intolerance (Immune Hypersensitivity)

Due to impaired immune regulation, benign inputs (foods, smells, mold) provoke overwhelming responses.[160] This parallels Phlegm Damp atop underlying Spleen/Kidney deficiency, which could be viewed as a preponderance of immune complexes atop APC depletion and FcγR over-activation.

N = Neuroinflammation

The blood-brain barrier becomes permeable, glial cells are inflamed, and cognitive dysfunction ensues.[161] In TCM, this is a collision of internal Wind[162], Heat, and Shaoyin axis disturbance.

---

[158] Wu, M. C. L., Italiano, E., Jarvis-Child, R., Alwis, I., Smythe, R., Albornoz, E. A., Noonan, J., Portelli, M., Baptista, M., Maclean, J., Noori, P., Yang, J., Lee, J. D., McFadyen, J. D., Sharland, A. F., Woodruff, T. M., Samson, A. L., Rapkiewicz, A., Barrett, T. J., Pham, A., Schoenwaelder, S. M., Yuan, Y., & Jackson, S. P. (2025). "Ischaemic endothelial necroptosis induces haemolysis and COVID-19 angiopathy." *Nature*, 618(7967), 123–130.

[159] Kell, D. B., Pretorius, E. and Zhao, H. (2025) A direct relationship between 'blood stasis' and fibrinaloid microclots in chronic, inflammatory and vascular diseases, and some traditional natural products approaches to treatment. *Pharmaceuticals*. 18, 712. https://doi.org/10.3390/ph18050712

[160] Yamada, D. H., Elsaesser, H., Lux, A., Timmerman, J. M., Morrison, S. L., de la Torre, J. C., Nimmerjahn, F., & Brooks, D. G. (2015). "Suppression of Fcγ-Receptor-Mediated Antibody Effector Function during Persistent Viral Infection." *Immunity*, 42(2), 379–390.

[161] Chen, Y., Yang, W., Chen, F., & Cui, L. (2022). "COVID-19 and cognitive impairment: neuroinvasive and blood–brain barrier dysfunction." *Journal of Neuroinflammation*, 19, Article 222.

[162] Wind(TCM): A primary external pathogenic factor characterized by sudden onset, movement, and variability. Wind is often the carrier for other pathogens (like Cold, Heat, or Damp) and is considered the "spearhead" of disease. It may

S = Suppression (Antigen Presentation, HPA - Axis, Mitochondria)

Whether due to persistent immune activation, neuroinflammation, low vagal tone, or mitochondrial stress, the hypothalamic-pituitary-adrenal axis weakens.[163] Cortisol and inflammation lose synchrony. The pattern here affects the Shaoyin channel system, where Heat hides in the deepest channels due to Yin exhaustion. One could also include Dr. Phair and Professor Ron Davis's Itaconate Shunt theory under "Suppression."[164]

Conclusion: Immune Injury as the Root, Deficiency as the Outcome and Precipitating Factor

The pathology of LPI may begin with injury to the immune system's core surveillance system. Effective treatment, from this perspective, needs to address that root: rather than focusing only on superficial symptoms or applying blanket tonification, an emphasis on restoring clarity at the immune interface, reviving APC function while managing inflammation, appears central.

In chronic illness, attempting to eradicate pathogens through aggressive antimicrobials often harms more than it helps, damaging the body's Qi and undermining the very systems needed for recovery. As Liu Bao-Yi teaches, our approach must be based on the state of Zheng Qi. If Zheng Qi is intact, the pathogen can be driven out directly by antimicrobials. But in most lingering and chronic conditions, Zheng Qi is depleted, and the priority must shift to restoring internal

---

manifest with symptoms such as tremors, spasms, vertigo, or migratory pain. Internally, Wind is associated with Liver dysfunction and may be linked to neurological or autoimmune activity in modern terms.

[163] Yavropoulou, M. P., Tsokos, G. C., Chrousos, G. P., & Sfikakis, P. P. (2022). "Protracted stress-induced hypocortisolemia may account for the clinical and immune manifestations of Long COVID." *Clinical Immunology*, 245, 109133.

[164] Itaconate Shunt Theory: A modern immunometabolic theory describing how activated macrophages and dendritic cells divert the TCA cycle by converting cis-aconitate into itaconate via the enzyme IRG1. This shift reduces energy production while exerting antimicrobial effects (by inhibiting bacterial isocitrate lyase) and anti-inflammatory control (via SDH inhibition and Nrf2 activation). While protective in acute settings, sustained itaconate production may impair antigen-presenting cell (APC) function, contributing to immune exhaustion and chronic illness states such as Long Covid and ME/CFS. In Chinese medicine terms, this represents a Yin-like metabolic retreat, akin to latent heat, toxin retention, or Zheng Qi deficiency.

function so the body can push the Lingering Pathogenic Illness out of hiding. In Chinese medicine, we do not seek eradication without restoration, so as to prevent relapse. The body must be cultivated like a garden, rather than constrained like a prison.

Chapter 5: Immunopathology in LPI Treatment: How to Recognize a Resolution Phase

Now that we have a working understanding of the likely pathomechanism behind Lingering Pathogenic Illness (LPI), we can turn to the nuance of treatment, specifically, what to expect as a patient begins to move through recovery. In this chapter, we'll explore the immunopathological processes that often precede symptom resolution and how they inform our expectations in clinical practice.

In the treatment of Lingering Pathogenic Illness, progress sometimes looks and feels like relapse. As the pathogen dislodges from the membrane source, the Shaoyang, or deeper Yin layers, symptoms may reappear, not as failure, but as movement and activation. When the immune system begins to earnestly re-engage after years of failed resolution, what emerges may feel worse before it feels better. But this is often the beginning of resolution, not its undoing.

The process of healing in LPI is not always gentle. It is the reanimation of a terrain that has been mostly suppressed. As the body begins to push out the latent evil, patients and practitioners can easily misinterpret progress in treatment as setbacks.

> "Lurking warm pathogens have many layers. After resolution and a cessation, one may proceed to evict through the next layer. Moreover, the pathogen of subsequent layers will invariably be more fixed than the first."[165]
>
> - *Liu Bao-Yi (1842–1901)*

---

[165] Text: *Wēn Rè Fēng Yuán* (《溫熱逢原》)
Section: 論伏溫邪 ("On Lurking Warm Pathogens")
Attributed Author: Liu Bao-Yi (劉保儀, 1842–1901)
Original: "伏溫之邪，層層深入，層層解去，然後為愈。每層之邪，較前一層更甚。"
Translation: "Lurking warm pathogens have many layers. After resolution and a cessation, one may proceed to evict through the next layer. Moreover, the pathogen of subsequent layers will invariably be more fixed than the first."

This changing and occasional worsening of symptoms is not diagnostic failure; it is a classical pattern. Pathogens generally resolve through reverse channel progression, exiting through the zones they once entered. One might think that the deeper the pathogen, the worse the immune reawakening, but this isn't necessarily true. Immunopathology from treatment is more acute when Zheng Qi is adequate and the pathogen is in the Yang-most layers of the body (due to excess). What's different about the deeper Yin layers is that they take much longer to resolve (due to deficiency).

Among the clearest signs of resolution in Lingering Pathogenic Illness are the following:

- Exacerbation of fatigue followed by a baseline improvement.
- Low-grade fever or subjective heat rising to the surface.
- Swollen lymph nodes or new-onset tenderness along channel junctions.
- Spontaneous sweating, particularly in the late afternoon or early morning.
- Irritability, restlessness, or emotional volatility.
- Thirst, especially with aversion to drinking.
- Dark yellow urine, or increased urinary frequency.
- Red and/or burning tongue tip or sides.
- Itching, maculae, transient rashes, or skin eruptions.
- Muscle and joint aches, particularly in areas previously stagnant.
- Brain fog, followed by brief windows of unusual clarity.
- Dizziness, palpitations, or mild chest discomfort.
- Return of appetite, sometimes preceded by nausea or bloating.
- Sudden improvement in bowel movements, often with loose stools or mild cramping beforehand.

These expressions reflect the emergence of the pathogen from depth toward the surface, and should be interpreted with attention to quality. For instance, when rashes appear during resolution, they are often sparse, scattered, and short-lived, sometimes fleeting enough to escape clinical observation. They may be itchy, mildly red, or macular, but not severely inflamed or blistered. These minor eruptions are signals of unburdening, of the immune system finally finding an outward path.

By contrast, when rashes are dense, persistent, or worsening, especially if pustulated and accompanied by fever, it may reflect a resurgence or deepening of the lingering pathogen rather than its resolution. In these cases, the patient may be acutely sick with a new infection and/or have a lingering pathogen that is acutely flaring due to a trigger.

"The outward expression of lingering pathogens must follow the weak spots in channel Qi: there is no certain route out of the body."[166]

- Lei Shou-Yi

Thus, resolution is rarely linear or elegant. It is *messy,* individual, and improvisational, depending entirely on when and where the body can open a door or window.

"Although it's inappropriate to use pungent and warm dispersing methods, one should also avoid using cold herbs that hinder the pathogen's outward movement."[167]

- Liu Bao-Yi

In other words, this process must be guided, not driven, and certainly not suppressed. What looks like a flare may in fact be a rare window of engagement.

To recognize these signs of resolution, such as fatigue that worsens before lifting, rashes that emerge and quickly fade, fleeting fevers, and brain fog followed by scattered moments of clarity, is to trust that healing, even when disorienting, has its own internal compass. It is the reengagement of the immune system, the clearing of

---

[166] Text: *Clinical Handbook of Internal Medicine, Volume 3: Qi Blood Fluid Channels*
Attributed Author: Lei Shou-Yi (雷守儀), as cited in Maclean, William; Lyttleton, Jane; Bayley, Mark; Taylor, Kathryn
Edition: 3rd Volume, 1st Edition
Publisher: Eastland Press, 2010
Quotation (as cited): "The outward expression of lingering pathogen must follow the weak spots in channel qi; there is no fixed route out of the body."
Note: This quote is attributed to Lei Shou-Yi in the context of lingering pathogens (伏邪) but may be a paraphrase or lineage transmission. The original source text is not explicitly cited.

[167] Text: *Wēn Rè Fēng Yuán* (溫熱逢原)
Section: Discussion of Treatment Principles for Residual Pathogens (論治伏邪)
Attributed Author: Liu Bao-Yi (劉保儀, 1842–1901)
Original: "不可用辛熱之劑，發散太過；亦不可用寒涼之藥，阻其外達。"
Translation: "Although it's inappropriate to use pungent and warm dispersing methods, one should also avoid using cold herbs that hinder the pathogen's outward movement."

a forgotten battlefield, the body's long memory surfacing to complete what was left unfinished.

Classical physicians such as Liu Bao-Yi emphasized that treatment strategies must adapt to the patient's constitution: direct expulsion in strong patients, balanced support and clearance in the moderately deficient, and Yin-nourishing defense in the severely depleted.

This layered strategy applies not just to treatment, but to interpretation. Some patients will move quickly through resolution, others must be gradually nourished while the body finds the strength to expel. Understanding the signs and symptoms along the way is what allows us to stay the course.

Treatment Duration in Lingering Pathogenic Illness

The recovery from Lingering Pathogenic Illness is not fast. It is not linear. And it is almost never a matter of weeks.

> *"Patients are often advised that treatment is not a matter of months but may be a matter of years. Ending therapy too early can result in a resurgence of symptoms that are often more difficult to treat, opposed to if therapy had not been interrupted. If symptoms of Gu Syndrome are relatively new and the patient presents as otherwise in good health, treatment duration is often only several months. However, if the patient was in poor health prior to the infection or if treatment was started long after symptoms first occurred, treatment is long-term and difficult."*[168]

This understanding is consistent with both classical and biomedical models of unresolved pathogenic illness. From an immunological standpoint, the mechanisms underlying LPI, such as APC dysfunction, FcγR-driven hyperreactivity, immune complex burden, mitochondrial dysfunction, and metabolic reprogramming, are

[168] Heidi Lovie. "Gu Syndrome, Lurking Pathogens, and Long Covid: An Old Take on a New Disease." *Medical Acupuncture*, vol. 33, no. 6, 2021, pp. 341–343. PMC8594969.

slow to reverse. Unlike acute infections, which resolve once the immune system clears a finite threat, Lingering Pathogenic Illness gets stuck as though in perpetual motion.

Factors That Influence Duration of Therapy:

- ❖ Timing: The longer the interval between pathogen exposure and initiation of treatment, the deeper the entrenchment of dysfunction.
- ❖ Baseline vitality: Those with robust Zheng Qi (or relatively intact APC tone and metabolic function) tend to recover faster.
- ❖ Pathogenic burden: Co-infections, immune complexes, and mucosal dysfunction increase recovery time.
- ❖ Tolerance thresholds: When immune tolerance is lost, restoring balance often takes sustained regulation before repair can begin.

Clinical Implications

In clinical practice, it's often necessary to counsel patients that "feeling better" is not the immediate goal. Rather, we aim to deconstruct the scaffolding of chronicity, to restore antigen processing, promote immune tolerance, and support long-term metabolic recovery. This means patients may need to cycle through herbal protocols for at least six months, depending on severity, resilience, and compliance.

Ending treatment too early, when fatigue lifts or food tolerance improves, can lead to a resurgence of deeper symptoms. Treatment should continue until the underlying deficiencies more or less resolve. As in classical Gu Syndrome, these relapses when abandoning treatment can sometimes be harder to treat than the original illness. Resolution must not only remove the pathogen or trigger but rebuild the host's immunologic self-regulation.

Chapter 6: Modifying Formulas with APC Stimulating Herbs for Lingering Pathogens

In this chapter, we'll explore specific herbs, both within and beyond the Chinese Materia Medica, that support antigen-presenting cell (APC) function. We'll then examine distinct patterns of Lingering Pathogenic Illness and outline corresponding formulas, including strategies for modification using immunologically active herbs.

Lingering Pathogenic Illness resists conventional treatments because it is not simply a deficiency or excess, not just heat or dampness, not purely internal or external. LPI is all of these at once, interwoven in a way that requires an adaptive, layered approach.

The heart of successful LPI treatment lies in a formula's ability to vent, clear, and nourish, all without causing deficiency or driving pathogens deeper. Venting herbs help push out residual evils when the body is ready. Damp-clearing herbs prevent the accumulation of turbidity that can impair the Spleen and trap pathogens. Yin and Qi tonifying herbs help restore the terrain damaged by the original immune injury.

Using only cold herbs to "purge heat" or tonics to "boost Qi" will fail if not modulated by attention to venting and drainage. *Even the most elegant traditional formulas must be modified carefully to accommodate the delicate balance of LPI treatment.* Herbs like Huang Qi (Astragalus membranaceus), Huang Jing (Polygonatum rhizoma), and Shan Yao (Dioscorea rhizoma) help nourish Qi and Yin while supporting immune resilience. Fu Ling (Poria cocos) mobilizes Damp without aggressively depleting fluids. And gentle venting herbs like Ge Gen (Pueraria lobata), when used appropriately, can invite pathogens to exit rather than linger in hidden tissue sites. Each formula must act like a prism, splitting each beam of pathology into its elemental components for removal.

It is important to note that in cases of lingering pathogenic illness, particularly where heat, toxicity, or stagnation are present, tonic herbs, especially rich Qi and Blood tonics, may be contraindicated on their own. Classical physicians often warned that premature supplementation could entrench evils or generate further complexity, a principle especially relevant in Gu-like conditions and residual heat patterns if we fail to properly vent and mobilize simultaneously.

We must treat lingering pathogens the way they behave, not how we wish they behaved. This is the ethos of LPI theory. Classical formulas must be modified, and in many cases, purged of extremes, especially cold and bitter medicinals that suppress rather than resolve. While cold herbs can extinguish surface heat, in patients with exhausted Qi and latent antigen, they often drive the pathogen deeper, impair digestion, and confuse immune signaling even further.

> "Although it is inappropriate to use pungent and warm dispersing methods, one should also avoid using cold herbs that hinder the pathogen's outward movement."
> - *Liu Bao-Yi* [169]

This warning is especially relevant for contemporary patients who are self-treating with "immune cleanses" or poorly guided antimicrobial regimens. Medicinals such as Berberine, Andrographis (Chuan Xin Lian), and Scutellaria (Huang Qin), while potent in their antimicrobial and anti-inflammatory effects, are inhibitory to antigen-presenting cells when used alone or in high doses over extended periods. Berberine (a compound found in many heat-clearing herbs), in particular, has been shown to induce apoptosis in dendritic cells, disrupting the very clarity needed to resolve immune dysfunction. While these herbs may relieve surface symptoms, they may also delay or prevent the unmasking of the core pattern. Essentially, the pathogen

[169] Text: *Wēn Rè Fēng Yuán* (溫熱逢原)
Section: Discussion of Treatment Principles for Residual Pathogens (論治伏邪)
Attributed Author: Liu Bao-Yi (劉保儀, 1842–1901)
Original: "不可用辛熱之劑，發散太過；亦不可用寒涼之藥，阻其外達。"
Translation: "Although it's inappropriate to use pungent and warm dispersing methods, one should also avoid using cold herbs that hinder the pathogen's outward movement."

must be able to move and expand. Overly cold and bitter medicinals force it to contract and hide.

Note an important paradox: we are using the following herbs and formulas to treat the disease as it manifests, particularly immunopathology (including that listed in Chapter 5) that *persists*. The following herbs and formulas are for when chronic illness manifests as distinct channel and level patterns, as though asking to be treated, verifiable in the tongue, pulse, and symptoms. The formulas that follow are for moderate-to-short-term use and should be immediately followed with formulas that fit the patient's changing presentation (listed later in Chapter 6). Alternatively, the following formulas can be stacked on top of my modern protocol formula offered in Chapter 7 (the next chapter) to suit an LPI patient's current presentation.

Core Medicinals for APC Repair

The following herbs and compounds have been selected for their combined traditional indications and *immune stimulatory* activity, particularly in the context of restoring immune recognition, regulating FcγR activity, and resolving antigen load. Each can be integrated flexibly depending on the patient's constitutional terrain and the layers (Wei, Qi, Shaoyang, Blood, etc.) currently affected. Almost all of the following herbs (except for Dan Shen, Lumbrokinase, and Yu Jin) support the immune system by upregulating immune function rather than acting as antimicrobial or purgative agents, an important distinction when modifying formulas for LPI.

Bai Zhi (*Angelicae Dahuricae Radix*)

Category: Release Exterior, Expel Wind

Temperature: Warm

Channels: Lung, Stomach

Traditional Functions: Expels Wind, opens the orifices, relieves pain, reduces swelling, and drains pus. Used for frontal headache, sinus congestion, toothache, and early-stage Wind invasion. Bai Zhi also addresses Wind-Damp obstruction and promotes discharge of purulent lesions, especially in the upper body.

Immunological Insight: Polysaccharides from *Angelica dahurica* have been shown to activate dendritic cells via TLR4 signaling, enhancing MHC II, CD86, and IL-12 expression. This promotes antigen presentation and Th1 rebalancing, making Bai Zhi useful where surface immune recognition is blunted. Coumarins further aid by clearing microbial biofilm and modulating microcirculation, linking immune vigilance with local detoxification and resolution.[170]

Clinical Use in LPI: Bai Zhi is used when superficial immune quiescence coexists with unresolved inflammatory debris, such as chronic sinusitis, brain fog, or dull frontal headache following viral illness. Its APC-stimulating and antimicrobial synergy make it ideal for revitalizing mucosal defense and antigen processing during recovery. In formulas, it often pairs with herbs that nourish or stabilize deeper Qi to prevent over-dispersion, such as Huang Jing or Mai Men Dong.

Cautions & Contraindications: Warm and dispersing; contraindicated in Yin deficiency with Heat, or in cases of Dryness or spontaneous sweating. Use cautiously in those with high sympathetic tone or vascular sensitivity, as coumarins may potentiate vasodilation. Avoid prolonged use in deficiency conditions without concurrent tonics.

Bai Zhu (*Atractylodis Macrocephalae Rhizoma*)

Category: Tonify Qi

Temperature: Warm

Channels: Spleen, Stomach

Traditional Functions: Strengthens the Spleen and augments Qi, dries Dampness, and stabilizes the Exterior. Traditionally used for fatigue, poor appetite, loose

---

[170] Kim HS, Shin BR, Lee HK, Park YS, Liu Q, Kim SY, Lee MK, Hong JT, Kim Y, Han SB. "Dendritic cell activation by polysaccharide isolated from Angelica dahurica." *Food Chem Toxicol.* 2013 May;55:241-7. doi: 10.1016/j.fct.2012.12.007. Epub 2012 Dec 14. PMID: 23246459.

stools, and spontaneous sweating due to Spleen Qi deficiency. It also calms the fetus and supports fluid metabolism, preventing pathogenic Damp accumulation.

Immunological Insight: Polysaccharides from *Atractylodes macrocephala* enhance macrophage and lymphocyte activity, promoting balanced cytokine release (IL-2, IL-10) and improving antigen processing under states of immune fatigue. Meanwhile, atractylenolides exert anti-inflammatory and antioxidative effects by inhibiting NF-κB, TLR4, and NLRP3 inflammasome signaling - mechanisms that restrain excess FcγR-mediated cytokine amplification while preserving antigen-presenting cell vigilance. This bidirectional regulation aligns with Bai Zhu's traditional role in strengthening the body's defenses without provoking inflammation. [171]

Clinical Use in LPI: Bai Zhu supports immune recovery in conditions marked by metabolic stagnation and immune depletion - particularly when post-infectious fatigue, poor digestion, or systemic Dampness coexist with chronic low-grade inflammation. In the LPI framework, it reinforces APC metabolism and membrane stability, helping recalibrate the balance between immune activation and resolution. Often paired with Huang Qi or Ling Zhi to fortify constitutional Qi and deepen restorative tone, or with Gou Teng and Ge Gen to couple immune renewal with microcirculatory flow.

Cautions & Contraindications: Warm and drying; contraindicated in Yin deficiency with Heat or dryness. Use cautiously in patients with excessive irritability, insomnia, or sympathetic overdrive. Prolonged use without replenishing fluids may aggravate Dryness; combine with moistening or Yin-supportive herbs as appropriate.

Che Qian Zi (*Plantaginis Semen*)

Category: Drains Dampness

Temperature: Cold

---

[171] Yong-Sheng Cui, Yi-Xuan Li, Si-Liang Jiang, An-Ning Song, Zheng Fu, Cai-Xia Dong, Zhi Yao, Wei Qiao, "Isolation, purification, and structural characterization of polysaccharides from Atractylodis Macrocephalae Rhizoma and their immunostimulatory activity in RAW264.7 cells," *International Journal of Biological Macromolecules*, Volume 163, 2020, Pages 270-278, ISSN 0141-8130, https://doi.org/10.1016/j.ijbiomac.2020.06.269.

Channels: Bladder, Kidney, Liver, Lung

Traditional Functions: Promotes urination to solidify stool, clears the eyes, expels phlegm, and clears Heat from the Liver and Lung.

Immunological Insight: Exhibits anti-inflammatory and immune-modulating effects via innate and adaptive pathways.[172] Also promotes lymphatic drainage and protects the intestinal mucosa.[173]

Clinical Use in LPI: Che Qian Zi is helpful in LPI cases with urinary discomfort, chronic sinus congestion, or inflammatory edema. It can gently support drainage of residual antigen burden through urination.

Cautions & Contraindications: Cold and slippery, avoid in cases of Kidney Yang deficiency or chronic loose stools. May cause digestive upset in patients with Spleen Qi deficiency. Use cautiously in patients on diuretics or lithium due to its mild diuretic effect and electrolyte-shifting potential.

Dan Shen (*Salviae Miltiorrhizae*)

Category: Blood-invigorating herb

Temperature: Slightly cold

Channels: Heart, Pericardium, Liver

Traditional Functions: Invigorates Blood, dispels stasis, cools Blood, calms the Shen (Spirit), and clears Heart Heat.

Immunological Insight: Exerts dual immunomodulatory and anti-fibrotic effects through inhibition of MMP2 and MMP9, making it particularly relevant for chronic inflammatory and post-viral tissue remodeling (may be helpful for hEDS). Tanshinone IIA and salvianolic acid B reduce pro-inflammatory cytokine expression via NF-κB and MAPK pathways while preserving vascular integrity and limiting

---

[172] Hu, J.-L., Nie, S.-P., Li, C., Fu, Z.-H., & Xie, M.-Y. (2014). "A novel polysaccharide from the seeds of *Plantago asiatica* L. induces dendritic cells maturation through toll-like receptor 4." *International Immunopharmacology*, 18(2), 236–243.

[173] Sahagún, A. M., Vaquera, J., García, J. J., Calle, Á. P., Diez, M.-J., Fernández, N., Loro, J. F., Portilla, H. O., & Sierra, M. (2015). "Study of the protective effect on intestinal mucosa of the hydrosoluble fiber *Plantago ovata* husk." *BMC Complementary and Alternative Medicine*, 15, 298.

immune-mediated tissue injury. Dan Shen, as a whole, is NOT immune stimulatory like the other herbs in this list despite containing immune stimulating tanshinones; it is immune-regulating.[174][175]

Clinical Use in LPI: Dan Shen is especially useful in cases of chronic inflammation, vascular stagnation, or neuroinflammation where Blood stasis and immune complex deposition are prominent. Appropriate at both Qi-Ying and Ying-Blood levels when APC exhaustion, endothelial injury, or fibrosis is suspected. Often paired with Qi tonics or Yin-nourishing herbs to support perfusion while preventing overstimulation.

Cautions & Contraindications: Cooling and Blood-moving, use with caution in patients with bleeding disorders, anticoagulant therapy, or menorrhagia. Contraindicated in pregnancy. May interact with blood thinners or antiplatelet medications. Not appropriate for cold-deficient constitutions unless balanced.

Dang Shen (*Codonopsis Radix*)

Category: Qi-tonifying herb

Temperature: Neutral

Channels: Lung, Spleen

Traditional Functions: Tonifies the middle burner, augments Lung Qi, generates fluids, and supports Blood production.

Immunological Insight: A gentle immunomodulator that enhances macrophage and dendritic cell function without overstimulation. Saponins and polysaccharides from Codonopsis support mucosal immunity, increase IgA secretion, and improve gut

[174] Chun-Yi Chuang a b, et al. "Salvianolic Acid a Suppresses MMP-2 Expression and Restrains Cancer Cell Invasion through Erk Signaling in Human Nasopharyngeal Carcinoma." *Journal of Ethnopharmacology*, Elsevier, 22 Jan. 2020, www.sciencedirect.com/science/article/abs/pii/S0378874119341340.

[175] Tang, Jiawen, and Xueying Zhao. "Research Progress on Regulation of Immune Response by Tanshinones and Salvianolic Acids of Danshen (Salvia Miltiorrhiza Bunge)." *MDPI*, Multidisciplinary Digital Publishing Institute, 7 Mar. 2024, www.mdpi.com/1420-3049/29/6/1201.

barrier integrity. Exhibits antioxidant and anti-apoptotic effects on immune cells, making it well-suited to states of low-grade immune depletion.[176]

Clinical Use in LPI: Preferred in mild-to-moderate Qi deficiency, especially when fatigue, poor digestion, and loose stools are present. Safer than Ren Shen in patients with possible smoldering pathogens, as it tonifies without trapping. Appropriate at the Wei and Qi levels, and in formulas addressing both recovery and tolerance. Often used to buffer dispersing herbs or harmonize multi-level strategies.

Cautions & Contraindications: Very safe and well-tolerated. Use with caution in extremely damp or phlegm-laden presentations unless paired with drying/aromatic herbs. May lose potency in highly collapsed constitutions, where Ren Shen or Huang Qi are more appropriate.

Fang Feng (*Saposhnikoviae Radix*)

Category: Wind-dispelling herb

Temperature: Slightly warm

Channels: Bladder, Liver, Spleen

Traditional Functions: Expels wind and alleviates pain, resolves dampness, and relieves spasms. Especially indicated for exterior wind-cold or wind-damp patterns with headache, body aches, or joint stiffness. Harmonizes the exterior without being overly drying or dispersing, making it suitable for deficiency states.

Immunological Insight: Fang Feng's polysaccharides and chromones exhibit immune-enhancing properties, including stimulation of macrophage activity, increased natural killer (NK) cell function, and modulation of cytokine production (notably IL-2 and IFN-γ). Its anti-allergic and anti-inflammatory actions reduce mast cell degranulation and histamine release, aligning with its traditional role in expelling "wind" and calming spasmodic or allergic reactions. The herb provides a mild immune stimulatory push, improving pathogen recognition and frontline

---

[176] Jiaxin Zhou a b, et al. "Codonopsis Pilosula Polysaccharide Alleviates Ulcerative Colitis by Modulating Gut Microbiota and SCFA/GPR/NLRP3 Pathway." *Journal of Ethnopharmacology*, Elsevier, 10 Oct. 2024, https://doi.org/10.1016/j.jep.2024.118928

defense without driving hyperinflammation, making it valuable in recovery from lingering infections.[177]

Clinical Use in LPI: Particularly useful at the Wei level, where immune surveillance at the surface is impaired, patients with chronic rhinitis, sinusitis, skin itching, or migratory body pain often respond. In formulas, Fang Feng supports the gentle activation of defensive Qi while harmonizing the action of stronger dispersing herbs. It bridges immune tonics and pathogen-expelling strategies, preventing excessive suppression. Works well when there is surface dysregulation with fatigue, allergic tendencies, or wind-damp joint pain.

Cautions & Contraindications: Generally safe and mild, but should be used cautiously in cases of marked Yin deficiency with heat signs, or in patients with pronounced dryness. In strongly deficient states, Fang Feng alone may be insufficient and should be paired with Qi tonics.

Fu Ling (*Poria Cocos*)

Category: Drain Damp, Tonify Spleen

Temperature: Neutral

Channels: Heart, Lung, Spleen, Kidney

Traditional Functions: Fu Ling drains Dampness, strengthens the Spleen, calms the Shen(Spirit), and promotes urination. It is a gentle stabilizer, excellent for those with fatigue, edema, or a foggy head.

Immunological Insight: Fu Ling supports the gut-immune axis, modulates inflammation, and encourages immune clarity in mucosal tissues.[178] It stabilizes terrain post-antibiotic use or after inappropriate cold herb regimens. Modulates macrophage activity and promotes homeostatic immune tolerance via polysaccharide-induced regulation of TLR4 and downstream MAPK/PI3K

---

[177] Cai-Xia Dong a b, et al. "Structural Characterization of Polysaccharides from Saposhnikovia Divaricata and Their Antagonistic Effects against the Immunosuppression by the Culture Supernatants of Melanoma Cells on Raw264.7 Macrophages." *International Journal of Biological Macromolecules*, Elsevier, 5 Mar. 2018, www.sciencedirect.com/science/article/abs/pii/S0141813018303271.

[178] Shi W, et al. "Structural characterization and adjuvant activity of a water soluble polysaccharide from Poria cocos." *Int J Biol Macromol.* 2024;273:133067. https://doi.org/10.1016/j.ijbiomac.2024.133067

pathways. Reduces systemic endotoxemia and supports gut-immune axis function. Has gentle adaptogenic and anxiolytic effects through GABA receptor modulation.

Clinical Use in LPI: Fu Ling is foundational for most patients, especially those with food intolerance, brain fog, or soft, swollen tongue presentations. It restores terrain without driving the pathogen in any direction prematurely.

Cautions & Contraindications: Generally safe and well-tolerated, but may cause mild dryness in very Yin-deficient individuals if used long-term. Use caution in cases with true fluid deficiency without signs of Dampness. May interact with diuretics; monitor fluid balance closely in polypharmacy settings.

Ge Gen (*Pueraria Radix* / Kudzu)

Category: Release Exterior

Temperature: Cool

Channels: Spleen, Stomach

Traditional Functions: Ge Gen releases the exterior, generates fluids, and relaxes muscles, especially in the neck and upper back. It also raises Yang Qi and is used for diarrhea, fever without sweating, and stiffness.

Immunological Insight: Puerarin supports glymphatic drainage and improves microvascular flow, relevant for patients with sinus pressure, cognitive fog, or lymphatic stagnation.[179] Ge Gen also induces dendritic cell maturation and reduces TNF-α and IL-6.[180] Isoflavones such as puerarin dampen FcγR-triggered ROS generation and restore endothelial nitric-oxide coupling, linking vascular repair to immune quiescence. Its upward movement and fluid-generating properties make it ideal for dysautonomia and post-viral myofascial pain syndromes.

Clinical Use in LPI: Ge Gen is especially useful in upper burner constraint, sinus congestion, or muscle-bound "surface heat" that cannot release. It clears without

---

[179] Wu, X.-D., Wang, C., Zhang, Z.-Y., Fu, Y., Liu, F.-Y., & Liu, X.-H. (2014). "Puerarin attenuates cerebral damage by improving cerebral microcirculation in spontaneously hypertensive rats." *Evidence-Based Complementary and Alternative Medicine*, 2014, Article ID 408501.

[180] Han SB, et al. "A polysaccharide isolated from Pueraria lobata enhances maturation of murine dendritic cells." *Int J Biol Macromol.* 2013;52:184-191 https://doi.org/10.1016/j.ijbiomac.2012.09.011

chilling and improves peripheral immune clearance, especially effective when paired with Jie Geng or Niu Xi.

Cautions & Contraindications: Use with caution in patients with a cold from deficiency, especially those prone to diarrhea, as it can be slightly cooling and dispersing. May lower blood pressure; use cautiously in hypotensive individuals or those on antihypertensive medications. Avoid in patients with significant Spleen Qi deficiency unless balanced.

Gou Teng (*Uncariae Ramulus cum Uncis* / Cat's Claw)

Category: Extinguish Wind and alleviate spasms

Temperature: Slightly cool

Channels: Liver, Pericardium

Traditional Functions: Calms Liver Yang and internal Wind, clears Heat, pacifies rising Liver Fire, and relieves tremors, spasms, or dizziness. Traditionally used for convulsions, hypertension, and neurogenic agitation.

Immunological Insight: Alkaloids and triterpenes in Gou Teng (notably rhynchophylline, isorhynchophylline, and uncarinic acids) have demonstrated immunomodulatory and dendritic cell-activating properties in vitro. These compounds promote APC maturation and IL-12 expression via TLR4-mediated signaling, biasing toward Th1 restoration while restraining excessive neuroinflammatory cascades.[181] In neural tissue, Gou Teng reduces microglial overactivation and preserves synaptic integrity, indicating a bidirectional immune-regulatory role - activating surveillance where deficient, yet suppressing excitotoxic inflammation in chronic states.

Clinical Use in LPI: Gou Teng is used where immune dysregulation and neuroinflammatory "wind" coexist, such as post-viral autonomic lability, tremor, tinnitus, or sleep dysrhythmia. It supports dendritic cell recalibration and reduces

---

[181] Umeyama A, Yahișa Y, Okada M, Okayama E, Uda A, Shoji N, Lee JJ, Takei M, Hashimoto T. "Triterpene esters from Uncaria rhynchophylla drive potent IL-12-dependent Th1 polarization." *J Nat Med.* 2010 Oct;64(4):506-9. doi: 10.1007/s11418-010-0438-1. Epub 2010 Jun 29. PMID: 20585989.

glial hyperexcitability, making it a key herb for neuroimmune balance within the LPI framework. In combination with mitochondrial tonics and APC-supporting herbs, it helps restore the rhythm of antigen presentation and central-peripheral signaling.

Cautions & Contraindications: Cold and dispersing; prolonged use or excessive dosage may weaken Spleen Qi or induce dizziness in those with underlying deficiency. Avoid in cases of pronounced Qi or Yang deficiency, or when internal Wind arises from Blood deficiency rather than Heat. Use with care in hypotensive patients.

Huang Jing (*Polygonati Rhizoma* / Solomon's Seal)

Category: Qi and Yin tonic

Temperature: Neutral to slightly warm

Channels: Lung, Spleen, Kidney

Traditional Functions: Tonifies Qi and Yin, moistens the Lungs, strengthens the Spleen, and nourishes the Kidneys.

Immunological Insight: Shown to enhance immune function and mitochondrial metabolism, especially under stress-induced states. Exhibits protective effects on APCs and promotes homeostatic recovery after inflammation.[182]

Clinical Use in LPI: Huang Jing is particularly well-suited to convalescence and rebuilding. In cases of severe fatigue with metabolic downregulation and endocrine dysregulation (e.g., HPA-axis suppression), this herb serves as a gentle anchor to rebuild immune plasticity and systemic tone.

Cautions & Contraindications: Rich, sweet, and cloying; may aggravate Dampness or cause bloating in those with weak digestion or Spleen deficiency. Avoid in patients with phlegm-Damp, or a thick tongue coating, unless carefully balanced. Not suitable during the early stages of acute infection.

---

[182] Liu, R., Zhang, X., Cai, Y., Xu, S., Xu, Q., Ling, C., Li, X., Li, W., Liu, P., & Liu, W. (2024). "Research progress on medicinal components and pharmacological activities of *Polygonatum sibiricum*." *Journal of Ethnopharmacology*, 328, 118024.

Huang Qi (*Astragalus Membranaceus*)

Category: Tonify Qi

Temperature: Slightly warm

Channels: Lung, Spleen

Traditional Functions: Huang Qi tonifies Spleen and Lung Qi, consolidates the exterior, promotes wound healing, and raises the Yang of the middle burner. It is commonly used to treat spontaneous sweating, fatigue, prolapse, and general weakness.[183]

Immunological Insight: Modern pharmacology confirms Huang Qi's effects on dendritic cell maturation, T-cell stimulation, and enhanced production of IL-12, an important cytokine for antigen presentation and antiviral immunity. It also reduces TNF-α and promotes mucosal immunity, making it an ideal terrain stabilizer in immune-exhausted patients.[184] By normalizing macrophage FcγR balance - enhancing inhibitory FcγRIIb expression while restraining FcγR-mediated NF-κB activation - Huang Qi moderates over-amplified antibody-driven inflammation without impairing immune recognition. It supports barrier immunity, reduces viral replication, and protects against immunosenescence by upregulating telomerase. It also exhibits mild anti-fibrotic activity and promotes lymphatic drainage.

Clinical Use in LPI: In patients with low-grade fever, post-exertional crashes, or frequent infections, Huang Qi reinforces the body's surface defense while restoring APC tone without triggering excess inflammation. It is especially useful when paired with herbs like Fu Ling or Ling Zhi to address Qi deficiency with Phlegm-Damp.

Cautions & Contraindications: Generally well-tolerated. Use with caution in patients with autoimmune activation or very robust inflammatory presentations unless properly balanced by the rest of the formula.

---

[183] Unless otherwise noted, herbal actions and properties are referenced from: Bensky, Dan, et al. Chinese Herbal Medicine: Materia Medica. 3rd ed., Eastland Press, 2004

[184] Yu JC, et al. "Application of dendritic cells in tumor immunotherapy and progress in the mechanism of anti-tumor effect of Astragalus polysaccharide modulating dendritic cells: a review." *Biomed Pharmacother.* 2022;155:113541 https://doi.org/10.1016/j.biopha.2022.113541

Hu Zhang (*Polygoni Cuspidati Rhizoma*)

Category: Herbs that invigorate Blood and clear Heat

Temperature: Cold

Channels: Liver, Gallbladder, Lung

Traditional Functions: Clears Heat, resolves Dampness, invigorates Blood, transforms phlegm, and relieves toxicity.

Immunological Insight: Rich in resveratrol, Hu Zhang possesses antiviral, anti-inflammatory, and antifibrotic properties. It may inhibit pathogenic persistence in endothelial and connective tissues.[185]

Clinical Use in LPI: Useful in post-viral syndromes where vascular dysfunction, fibrosis, or connective tissue involvement (e.g., joint stiffness, tinnitus, dizziness) are prominent. Use with caution in patients with cold patterns.

Cautions & Contraindications: Cooling and dispersing, use cautiously in cases of Qi deficiency, cold conditions, or weak digestion. May potentiate the effects of anticoagulant or antiplatelet drugs due to its resveratrol content. Not recommended in pregnancy due to limited safety data and its downward-moving nature.

Jie Geng (*Platycodi Radix*)

Category: Transform Phlegm, Open the Lungs

Temperature: Neutral

Channels: Lung

Traditional Functions: Jie Geng opens the Lungs, guides the effects of other herbs upward, transforms Phlegm, and benefits the throat. It is commonly used in cough, hoarseness, and chest oppression.

Immunological Insight: Modern research shows Jie Geng enhances mucosal immune clearance, improves airway barrier integrity, and may support upper airway

---

[185] Ke, J., Li, M., Xu, S., Ma, J., Liu, M., & Han, Y. (2023). "Advances for pharmacological activities of *Polygonum cuspidatum* – A review." *Pharmaceutical Biology*, 61(1), 177–188 https://doi.org/10.1080/13880209.2022.2158349

microbiome balance, making it relevant in persistent sinus or laryngeal dysfunction.[186]

Clinical Use in LPI: Jie Geng is important when pathogens begin to surface through the Lung/Shaoyang axis. It supports the emergence of lingering pathogens and prevents them from stagnating in the upper Jiao. Use it to prevent reburial during immune unmasking.

Cautions & Contraindications: Acrid and ascending, use with caution in cases of chronic cough with Yin deficiency or heat signs unless balanced with moistening herbs. May aggravate dry throat or hoarseness when overused. Avoid in patients with hemoptysis due to Lung Yin deficiency or when there is significant Qi depletion.

Ku Shen (*Sophorae Flavescentis Radix*)

Category: Clears Heat, Dries Dampness

Temperature: Cold

Channels: Bladder, Liver, Stomach, Large Intestine

Traditional Functions: Clears Damp-Heat from the lower burner, promotes urination, kills parasites, and stops itching. Used topically or internally for skin disorders, leukorrhea, and Damp-Heat dysentery.

Immunological Insight: Possesses strong anti-inflammatory and antimicrobial activity, especially against gram-positive and gram-negative bacteria. Inhibits histamine release, modulates NF-κB signaling, and may attenuate Th2-dominant inflammation.[187] It also supports gut barrier function and downregulates inflammatory cytokine expression.[188]

---

[186] Gao, P., Li, X., Ding, J., Peng, B., Munir, M., Liu, F., Chao, L., Li, C., Wang, L., Ma, J., & Zhang, G. (2025). "Antiviral and Immune Enhancement Effect of *Platycodon grandiflorus* in Viral Diseases: A Potential Broad-Spectrum Antiviral Drug." *Molecules*, 30(4), 831 https://doi.org/10.3390/molecules30040831

[187] Wang, Meng-Chun, et al. "Sophoraflavanone G from Sophora Flavescens Ameliorates Allergic Airway Inflammation by Suppressing Th2 Response and Oxidative Stress in a Murine Asthma Model." *MDPI, Multidisciplinary Digital Publishing Institute*, 29 May 2022, https://doi.org/10.3390/ijms23116104

[188] Chen M, Ding Y, Tong Z. "Efficacy and safety of *Sophora flavescens* (Kushen)-based traditional Chinese medicine in the treatment of ulcerative colitis: Clinical evidence and potential mechanisms." *Front Pharmacol*. 2022;13:934611. https://doi.org/10.3389/fphar.2020.603476

Clinical Use in LPI: Ku Shen is particularly helpful in LPI presentations with lower burner Damp-Heat, urogenital inflammation, gut-lung axis dysbiosis, or histamine excess. Useful in patients with inflammatory skin conditions, loose stools with urgency, or urinary discomfort related to microbial or mycotoxin burden.

Cautions & Contraindications: Bitter and cold; may damage the Spleen and Stomach with long-term use. Use cautiously in deficient or cold constitutions, or when loose stools and poor appetite are present. Avoid during pregnancy and in patients with constitutional dryness.

Ling Zhi (*Ganoderma* / Reishi mushroom)

Category: Tonify Qi, Calm Spirit

Temperature: Neutral

Channels: Heart, Lung, Liver

Traditional Functions: Ling Zhi nourishes the Heart, tonifies Qi and Blood, and calms the Shen (Spirit). It is considered an herb of longevity and spirit stabilization, often used in deficiency syndromes with emotional or constitutional fragility.

Immunological Insight: Ling Zhi is a broad-spectrum immune modulator, reducing IL-6 and TNF-α, MMP2, and MMP9 while supporting natural killer cell activity, dendritic cell function, and redox balance.[189][190] Triterpenoids from Ling Zhi down-regulate FcγR-linked Syk/NF-κB signaling, tempering cytokine release and oxidative burst in macrophages. It also exhibits neuroprotective and mitochondrial-stabilizing effects.[191]

Clinical Use in LPI: Ideal for patients with post-viral anhedonia, neuroinflammation, or those who are emotionally dysregulated after illness. Ling

---

[189] Zhang, Y., Li, S., Wang, X., Zhang, L., Cheung, P. C. K., & Ooi, V. E. C. (2002). "Regulation on maturation and function of dendritic cells by Ganoderma lucidum polysaccharides." *Immunology Letters*, 83(3), 163–169, https://doi.org/10.1016/S0165-2478(02)00087-1

[190] Rizal, A., Sandra, F., Fadlan, M. R., & Sargowo, D. (2020). "Ganoderma lucidum Polysaccharide Peptide Reduce Inflammation and Oxidative Stress in Patient with Atrial Fibrillation." *The Indonesian Biomedical Journal*, 12(4), 384–389, DOI:10.18585/inabj.v12i4.1244

[191] Ren, Zl., Wang, Cd., Wang, T. *et al.* "*Ganoderma lucidum* extract ameliorates MPTP-induced parkinsonism and protects dopaminergic neurons from oxidative stress via regulating mitochondrial function, autophagy, and apoptosis." *Acta Pharmacol Sin* 40, 441–450 (2019). https://doi.org/10.1038/s41401-018-0077-8

Zhi soothes without sedating and restores without overstimulation. It is especially beneficial for Shaoyin patterns, insomnia, or subtle dysautonomia.

Cautions & Contraindications: Generally well-tolerated, but may cause mild digestive upset in sensitive individuals. Use with caution in patients on immunosuppressants or anticoagulants, as Ling Zhi has mild immune-modulating and antiplatelet effects. Discontinue prior to surgery. Rarely, it can provoke overstimulation in very deficient patients if dosed too high initially.

Lu Hui (*Aloe*)

Category: Downward-draining purgatives

Temperature: Cold

Channels: Large Intestine, Liver, Stomach

Traditional Functions: Drains Liver Fire, clears heat and guides out accumulation, kills parasites.

Immunological Insight: Enhances immune function by activating TLR3/7/8/9, induces DC maturation (upregulates CD80, CD86, and MHC II), and reduces IL-8, TNF-α, IL-6, and IL-1.[192]

Clinical Use: Lu Hui (Aloe) is best known for its bitter, cold, and descending nature. While traditionally used for constipation with heat signs, in the context of Lingering Pathogenic Illness, it offers two crucial actions: it clears internal heat that is often bound in the digestive tract or Liver/Gallbladder axis, and it supports pathogen resolution by gently promoting downward movement and detoxification.

Cautions & Contraindications: Harshly downward-draining, contraindicated in pregnancy, during menstruation (with heavy bleeding), or in cases of deficiency Cold. Use cautiously in patients with sensitive digestion or chronic diarrhea. Not suitable for long-term use without addressing the root causes of stagnation or heat.

---

[192] Lee CK, et al. "Acemannan purified from Aloe vera induces phenotypic and functional maturation of immature dendritic cells." *Int Immunopharmacol.* 2001;1(7):1275-1284. https://doi.org/10.1016/S1567-5769(01)00052-2

Lumbrokinase (*Lumbricus Rubellus*)

Category: Open Channels / Resolve Phlegm / Move Blood

Temperature: Neutral

Channels: Liver, Bladder, Lung

Traditional Functions: In its classical form (Di Long), it opens the collaterals, calms wheezing, promotes urination, and resolves Heat lodged in the channels.

Immunological Insight: Not immune stimulatory. The enzyme isolate lumbrokinase has fibrinolytic properties, helping to break down fibrin, biofilms, and microclots.[193][194] These microstructures often protect viral or fungal debris from immune clearance and contribute to vascular insufficiency and tissue hypoxia in LPI.

Clinical Use in LPI: Lumbrokinase is crucial when microcirculation is impaired, particularly in cases of peripheral cold, brain fog, or post-Covid coagulation patterns. It increases tissue penetration of herbs and helps release antigens from biofilm-protected zones.

Cautions & Contraindications: Not a traditional Chinese herb, but derived from earthworms and used for its fibrinolytic (clot-dissolving) activity. Contraindicated in patients with active bleeding, bleeding disorders, or those on anticoagulant or antiplatelet medications (e.g., warfarin, aspirin). Discontinue prior to surgery or dental procedures. Use cautiously during menstruation in patients with heavy flow.

Mai Men Dong (*Ophiopogonis Radix*)

Category: Tonify Yin

Temperature: Slightly cold

Channels: Heart, Lung, Stomach

Traditional Functions: Mai Men Dong nourishes Lung and Stomach Yin, generates fluids, clears Heart Heat, and calms irritability. It is used for dry cough, thirst, insomnia, and palpitations.

---

[193] Cooper, E. (2009). "New Enzyme Complex Isolated From Earthworms Is Potent Fibrinolytic." *Clinical Education.*

[194] Cooper, E. (2009). "Two Doctors Report on the Use of Lumbrokinase in Lyme Disease: This Enzyme Complex Helps Potentiate Antibiotics and Antimicrobials." *Clinical Education.*

Immunological Insight: This herb supports mucosal integrity and immune tolerance as well as APC maturation, especially in airway and gut tissues.[195] It acts as a cytokine modulator and helps reduce lingering inflammatory loops that dry out fluids and exhaust the axis between digestion and immunity.[196]

Clinical Use in LPI: Particularly helpful when dryness coexists with irritability, shortness of breath, or post-viral throat sensitivity. Mai Men Dong helps repair tissues and improve absorption, allowing deeper tonics like Huang Jing or Shan Yao to take hold.

Cautions & Contraindications: Yin-nourishing and moistening may aggravate Dampness or phlegm if digestion is weak. Use cautiously in patients with Spleen deficiency, bloating, or a thick, greasy tongue. Not recommended in conditions with significant exterior excess or Cold accumulation.

Neem (*Azadirachta Indica*)

Category: Clear Heat and Resolve Toxicity

Temperature: Cold

Channels: Liver, Stomach, Blood

Traditional Functions: Clears heat, resolves toxicity, disperses wind-heat from the skin, and cools the Blood.

Immunological Insight: Potent immunomodulator with demonstrated antiviral, antifungal, and antibacterial properties. Regulates inflammatory cytokines (e.g., TNF-α, IL-6) and inhibits overactivation of TLR pathways. Supports APC-mediated recognition of pathogens while dampening excessive inflammatory signaling.[197][198]

---

[195] Zhu, N., Lv, X., Wang, Y., Li, J., Liu, Y., Lu, W., Yang, L., Zhao, J., Wang, F., & Zhang, L. W. (2016). "Comparison of immunoregulatory effects of polysaccharides from three natural herbs and cellular uptake in dendritic cells." *International Journal of Biological Macromolecules*, 93(Pt A), 940–951.

[196] Li, N., Zhang, J.-Y., Zeng, K.-W., Zhang, L., Che, Y.-Y., & Tu, P.-F. (2012). "Anti-inflammatory homoisoflavonoids from the tuberous roots of *Ophiopogon japonicus*." *Fitoterapia*, 83(6), 1042–1045.

[197] Kumar S, et al. "Neem (Azadirachta indica): prehistory to contemporary medicinal uses to humankind." *Asian Pac J Trop Biomed.* 2016;6(7):505-514.

[198] Baral R, et al. "Neem leaf glycoprotein matures myeloid derived dendritic cells and optimizes anti-tumor T cell functions." *Vaccine.* 2010;28(5):1241-1252. https://doi.org/10.1016/j.vaccine.2009.11.018

Clinical Use in LPI: Useful in cases of residual heat, low-grade infection, or reactivated pathogens. Especially helpful when skin eruptions, fungal overgrowth, or latent damp-heat are present alongside immune dysregulation. Its immunomodulatory action makes it appropriate when low-level toxicity or microbial burden is suspected in a deficient terrain.

Cautions & Contraindications: Cold and bitter, use cautiously in patients with Qi or Yang deficiency, fatigue with cold signs, or poor digestive fire. It may suppress fertility and should be avoided during pregnancy or when fertility is desired. Not suitable for long-term use in Yin-deficient patients without accompanying tonics.

Niu Xi (*Achyranthis Bidentatae Radix*)

Category: Invigorate Blood, Guide Downward

Temperature: Neutral

Channels: Liver, Kidney

Traditional Functions: Niu Xi invigorates Blood, strengthens sinews and bones, clears Damp-Heat in the lower burner, and directs Fire or Blood downward.

Immunological Insight: Niu Xi promotes APC function, improves peripheral circulation, reduces stagnation in the lower Jiao, and facilitates drainage of immune debris.[199] It may reduce immune congestion in pelvic or lymphatic tissues.

Clinical Use in LPI: Niu Xi is an essential guide herb in "upward-rising" LPI patterns, headaches, mouth sores, agitation, or any syndrome in which Heat is stuck and unable to descend. It clears the path for exit.

Cautions & Contraindications: Strongly descending, use with caution in pregnancy, especially in cases with threatened miscarriage or uterine bleeding. Avoid in patients with hypermenorrhea or bleeding disorders unless appropriately balanced. Not appropriate in cases of prolapse with significant Qi deficiency unless combined with strong tonics.

---

[199] Shan F, et al. "Modulation of phenotypic and functional maturation of murine dendritic cells by purified Achyranthes bidentata polysaccharide." *Int Immunopharmacol.* 2011;11(8):1103-1108. https://doi.org/10.1016/j.intimp.2011.03.006

Ren Shen (*Ginseng Radix*)

Category: Qi-tonifying herb

Temperature: Slightly warm

Channels: Lung, Spleen, Heart

Traditional Functions: Powerfully tonifies Yuan Qi, strengthens the Spleen and Lungs, generates fluids, and calms the Shen.

Immunological Insight: Potent immunostimulant and adaptogen. Ginsenosides modulate both innate and adaptive immune responses by influencing dendritic cell maturation, T-cell proliferation, and cytokine balance (notably IL-2, IL-6, IFN-γ). Enhances NK cell function and promotes HPA axis resilience.[200] Its Qi-restorative properties also correlate with improvements in mitochondrial ATP production and antioxidant defenses.

Clinical Use in LPI: Reserved for cases of profound Qi depletion with fatigue, dyspnea, hypotension, or cognitive collapse. Particularly useful in late-stage or post-viral syndromes with autonomic failure, poor postural tone, and metabolic shutdown. Appropriate for Qi-Ying level collapse, especially when other tonics are insufficient. May stabilize mast cell activation and reduce vascular permeability via HPA support.

Cautions & Contraindications: Very tonifying, contraindicated in febrile conditions or active pathogen presence. May aggravate heat, stagnation, or excess Yang. Use with caution in hypertension, mania, or insomnia. May interact with MAO inhibitors, stimulants, or corticosteroids. *In cases of Gu syndrome or other smoldering pathogen conditions, especially as described in Qing dynasty literature (e.g., Ye Tianshi, Liu Bao-Yi), Ren Shen was often avoided for fear of "trapping" the pathogen by tonifying too strongly without adequate clearing.*

Rou Cong Rong (*Cistanches Herba*)

Category: Tonify Yang

[200] Kang, S., & Min, H. (2012). "Ginseng, the "Immunity Boost": The Effects of Panax ginseng on the Immune System." *Journal of Ginseng Research*, 36(4), 354–368. https://doi.org/10.5142/jgr.2012.36.4.354

Temperature: Warm

Channels: Kidney, Large Intestine

Traditional Functions: Rou Cong Rong tonifies Kidney Yang, benefits essence and Blood, strengthens sinews, and moistens the intestines. It is used for impotence, infertility, cold pain in the lower back and knees, and constipation due to dryness from Blood or Yin deficiency.

Immunological Insight: Rou Cong Rong enhances dendritic cell and macrophage activity while balancing Th1/Th2 cytokine output. It supports mitochondrial function and ATP generation in immune and endocrine tissues, helping restore vitality after prolonged depletion. The herb's phenylethanoid glycosides (notably echinacoside and acteoside) exhibit neuroprotective and anti-aging effects through antioxidant and Nrf2-mediated pathways, countering immunosenescence and fatigue seen in chronic infection and post-viral syndromes.[201]

Clinical Use in LPI: Rou Cong Rong is a key restorative herb in Yin-deficient LPI recovery phases, particularly when exhaustion, cold extremities, and poor libido coexist with immune hyporesponsiveness. It bridges Qi and Essence restoration, strengthening the Kidney-Brain-Marrow axis and aiding repair of deep energetic depletion following pathogenic injury.

Cautions & Contraindications: Avoid Rou Cong Rong in patterns with exuberant Heat, constipation from excess, or Yin deficiency with Heat signs. Use cautiously in early or acute stages of infection when stimulation of Yang may trap Heat.

Sang Ji Sheng (*Taxilli Herba*)

Category: Herbs that tonify Yin and expel Wind-Damp

Temperature: Neutral

Channels: Kidney, Liver

---

[201] Lei H, Wang X, Zhang Y, Cheng T, Mi R, Xu X, Zu X, Zhang W. "Herba Cistanche (Rou Cong Rong): A Review of Its Phytochemistry and Pharmacology." *Chem Pharm Bull* (Tokyo). 2020;68(8):694-712. doi: 10.1248/cpb.c20-00057. PMID: 32741910.

Traditional Functions: Tonifies the Liver and Kidneys, strengthens the sinews and bones, expels Wind-Damp, and calms the fetus.

Immunological Insight: Flavonoids from Sang Ji Sheng have demonstrated immunoregulatory effects, especially in promoting hematopoietic function and modulating inflammatory cytokines such as TNF-α and IL-6.[202]

Clinical Use in LPI: Particularly useful in cases where inflammatory joint pain and postural instability follow immune injury. Its affinity for sinews and bones makes it appropriate in long-standing cases where Wei Qi has failed to reach peripheral tissues.

Cautions & Contraindications: Generally mild and well-tolerated. Use cautiously in very cold-damp constitutions or with loose stools, as it is neutral to slightly cool and may weaken digestion if used excessively.

Shan Yao (*Dioscoreae Rhizoma*)

Category: Qi tonic

Temperature: Neutral

Channels: Kidney, Lung, Spleen

Traditional Functions: Tonifies Spleen and Lung Qi, stabilizes and secures the essence, and nourishes Yin.

Immunological Insight: Shan Yao has demonstrated antioxidant and immune-enhancing properties. It appears to modulate the balance of T-helper cells and stimulate macrophage phagocytosis in vitro. Its stabilizing effect may support gut-associated immune tissue integrity.[203]

Clinical Use in LPI: For patients whose immune injury has disrupted the gut-lung axis, or who have symptoms of both Qi deficiency and digestive weakness, Shan

---

[202] Zhang, L., Koyyalamudi, S. R., Jeong, S. C., Reddy, N., Bailey, T., & Longvah, T. (2013). "Immunomodulatory activities of polysaccharides isolated from *Taxillus chinensis* and *Uncaria rhyncophylla*." *Carbohydrate Polymers*, 98(2), 1458–1465.

[203] Park, S.-Y., Truong, V.-L., Jeon, S.-G., Choe, S.-Y., Rarison, R. H. G., Yoon, B.-H., Park, J.-W., Jeong, H.-J., & Jeong, W.-S. (2025). "Anti-inflammatory and prebiotic potential of ethanol extracts and mucilage polysaccharides from Korean yams (*Dioscorea polystachya* and *Dioscorea bulbifera*)." *Foods*, 14(2), 173.

Yao provides gentle support to barrier immunity and essence retention, particularly when fatigue and "leakiness" predominate.

Cautions & Contraindications: Very safe and tonifying, but its astringent nature may be inappropriate in cases of Dampness accumulation, or where stagnation needs to be dispersed. Use cautiously in patients with a thick tongue coating or phlegm-Damp presentations, unless balanced with moving or drying herbs.

Sheng Di Huang (*Rehmannia Radix*)

Category: Cool Blood, Nourish Yin

Temperature: Cold

Channels: Heart, Kidney, Liver

Traditional Functions: Sheng Di Huang nourishes Yin, cools the Blood, generates fluids, and clears Heat from the Ying and Blood levels. It is used in febrile illnesses, mouth sores, and dry mouth with low-grade fever.

Immunological Insight: It modulates inflammatory cytokines, supports antigen presentation, protects vascular and gastrointestinal endothelium, and provides deep cooling support without extinguishing surface defense.[204][205] It is especially suited to Yin deficiency from immune overactivation.

Clinical Use in LPI: Essential when the patient shows signs of residual heat with dryness, oral ulcers, or subtle Blood-level inflammation. Sheng Di pairs well with Fu Ling and Huang Qi in patients who run warm, have night sweats, or show red-tipped tongues with scant coating.

Cautions & Contraindications: Cold, heavy, and cloying, use with caution in patients with Spleen Qi deficiency, Dampness, or loose stools. May worsen digestive symptoms in weak or congested patients, unless balanced with aromatic or warming

---

[204] Jin JO, et al. "Rehmannia glutinosa polysaccharide promoted activation of human dendritic cells." *Int J Biol Macromol.* 2018;116:232-238.

[205] Li, X., Gui, R., Wang, X., Ning, E., Zhang, L., Fan, Y., Chen, L., Yu, L., Zhu, J., Li, Z., Wei, L., Wang, W., Li, Z., Wei, Y., & Wang, X. (2023). "Oligosaccharides isolated from *Rehmannia glutinosa* protect LPS-induced intestinal inflammation and barrier injury in mice." *Frontiers in Nutrition*, 10, 1139006.

herbs. Not appropriate during the early stages of acute infection unless clear heat signs are present.

Tai Zi Shen (*Pseudostellariae Radix*)

Category: Qi tonic

Temperature: Slightly cool

Channels: Lung, Spleen

Traditional Functions: Tonifies Qi, generates fluids, and nourishes Yin.

Immunological Insight: Enhances innate immunity by boosting NK cell activity and increasing secretion of immune-supportive cytokines. Supports APC activity without overstimulation, making it safer for patients with delicate immune tone.[206]

Clinical Use in LPI: Ideal substitute for Ren Shen in sensitive patients, or when an immunomodulating Qi tonic is needed without increasing internal heat. Particularly suited to post-viral syndromes with both Qi and Yin deficiency. Useful tonic for dysautonomia.

Cautions & Contraindications: Mild Qi and Yin tonic, generally safe, but may be too cloying for patients with Dampness, poor appetite, or bloating. Use cautiously in those with significant Spleen Qi deficiency, presenting with loose stools or phlegm accumulation. Avoid overuse in the early stages of external invasion.

Yu Jin (*Curcumae Radix*)

Category: Invigorate Blood, Clear Heat

Temperature: Cold

Channels: Heart, Liver, Lung

Traditional Functions: Yu Jin invigorates the Blood, moves Qi, clears Heat in the Heart and Liver, cools the Blood, and opens the orifices. It is traditionally used for

---

[206] Wong, C. K., Leung, K. N., Fung, K. P., & Choy, Y. M. (1994). "The immunostimulating activities of anti-tumor polysaccharides from *Pseudostellaria heterophylla*." *Immunopharmacology*, 28(1), 47–54.

constraint presenting as chest or hypochondriac pain, emotional distress, menstrual irregularities, and phlegm obstructing the Heart orifices.

Immunological Insight: Not immune stimulatory. Yu Jin downregulates IL-6, TNF-α, and other proinflammatory cytokines, while modulating microvascular tone and improving blood-brain barrier integrity. It shows neuroprotective effects through antioxidant and anti-inflammatory mechanisms, and may inhibit monoamine oxidase, supporting neurotransmitter balance in inflammatory mood disorders.[207]

Clinical Use in LPI: Yu Jin is especially useful in "Liver Fire with Blood constraint" LPI patterns, patients with irritability, chest oppression, cognitive fog, hormonal dysregulation, and neuroinflammatory presentations. It is also indicated when Blood stasis obstructs exit, such as in the lingering aftermath of viral illness with vascular or neurological sequelae. It pairs well with Chai Hu formulas, Blood-moving formulas, and herbs that nourish Yin or calm Shen.

Cautions & Contraindications: Avoid in patients with severe Cold from deficiency, or those with excessive menstrual bleeding unless properly balanced. Not indicated in cases of pure deficiency without stagnation. May counteract the effects of cloying tonics or resinous Qi supplements if not coordinated carefully.

Zhi Ban Xia (*Pinelliae Rhizoma Preparatum*)

Category: Transform Phlegm, Harmonize the Stomach

Temperature: Warm (when prepared)

Channels: Lung, Spleen, Stomach

Traditional Functions: Ban Xia transforms Cold Phlegm, dries Dampness, descends rebellious Qi, and harmonizes the Stomach. It is essential in vomiting, cough with phlegm, and fullness in the chest.

---

[207] Hu D, Gao J, Yang X, Liang Y. "A Comprehensive Mini-Review of Curcumae Radix: Ethnopharmacology, Phytochemistry, and Pharmacology." *Natural Product Communications*. 2021;16(5). doi:10.1177/1934578X211020628

Immunological Insight: Ban Xia may support immune clarity by supporting APCs, resolving gut-stored phlegm, improving bioavailability of herbs, and clearing the mucosal burden that contributes to antigen persistence.[208][209]

Clinical Use in LPI: Ban Xia is especially effective in patients with gut dysbiosis, poor appetite, post-nasal drip, or persistent throat clearing. It prevents herbs like Sheng Di or Fu Ling from stagnating, and ensures safe Yin nourishment in Damp-prone bodies.

Cautions & Contraindications: Toxic when unprepared; only the properly processed (Zhi) form should be used. Drying in nature, use with caution in cases of Yin deficiency or dryness. Contraindicated during pregnancy unless specifically indicated and properly balanced. It may be irritating to the throat in sensitive individuals.

Zhi Gan Cao (*Glycyrrhizae Radix Uralensis Preparatum*)

Category: Herbs that Tonify Qi

Temperature: Warm

Channels: Heart, Lung, Spleen, Stomach

Traditional Functions: Tonifies the Spleen and augments Qi, moistens the Lung to stop cough, moderates spasms and alleviates pain, harmonizes other herbs, and relieves toxicity.

Immunological Insight: Zhi Gan Cao enhances immunogenic activity by modulating both innate and adaptive immune responses. Its primary constituent, glycyrrhizin, stimulates antigen-presenting cell (APC) function and promotes interferon production, enhancing antiviral defenses. It supports T-cell proliferation and macrophage activation, while also helping to restore immune tolerance by regulating dendritic cell activity. These effects make it useful in conditions of

---

[208] Wang, Y., Lu, C., Huang, H., Yao, S., Xu, C., Ye, Y., Gui, S., & Li, G. (2020). "A lipid-soluble extract of *Pinellia pedatisecta* Schott orchestrates intratumoral dendritic cell-driven immune activation through SOCS1 signaling in cervical cancer." *Journal of Ethnopharmacology*, 267, 112837.

[209] Tao, X., Liu, H., Xia, J., Zeng, P., Wang, H., Xie, Y., Wang, C., Cheng, Y., Li, J., Zhang, X., Zhang, P., Chen, S., Yu, H., & Wu, H. (2022). "Processed product (Pinelliae Rhizoma Praeparatum) of *Pinellia ternata* (Thunb.) Breit. alleviates the allergic airway inflammation of cold phlegm via regulation of PKC/EGFR/MAPK/PI3K-AKT signaling pathway." *Journal of Ethnopharmacology*, 295, 115449.

immune exhaustion or suppression following prolonged viral or inflammatory states.[210]

Clinical Use in LPI: Supports recovery in patients with depleted Qi, chronic cough, or autonomic dysregulation. Its harmonizing effect makes it valuable in complex formulas where harsh ingredients or detoxifying agents risk damaging the Spleen and Stomach. It may support adrenal resilience in states of prolonged stress or exhaustion.

Cautions & Contraindications: Prolonged use or high doses may cause fluid retention, hypertension, or pseudoaldosteronism, especially in sensitive individuals. Use with caution in cases of edema, hypokalemia, or hypertension. Not recommended for patients taking potassium-wasting diuretics or corticosteroids without monitoring.

Channel-Based Presentations of Lingering Pathogenic Illness

Before diving into more detailed formula-based symptomology, I'll reintroduce this brief list of channel/level-based symptomology to map the broader terrain. These should mirror how symptoms tend to cluster along channel dynamics in LPI patients. Know that LPI patients can have multiple channel-based presentations as the heat pathogen moves in and out of multiple layers of deficiency, and that we should treat the dominant or more superficial pattern first:

- **Wei Level / Taiyang (Surface Dysregulation):**

Aversion to wind, cold sensitivity, and heat effusion, allergic rhinitis, chronic sinusitis, clammy or itchy skin, persistent occipital/neck pain and headaches, generalized body pain, fatigue with mild exertion, and a floating pulse.

[210] Narges Bordbar a, et al. "The Effect of Glycyrrhizin on Maturation and T Cell Stimulating Activity of Dendritic Cells." *Cellular Immunology*, Academic Press, 1 Dec. 2012, www.sciencedirect.com/science/article/abs/pii/S0008874912002079.

❖ **Shaoyang (Membrane Source Constraint):**

Sore, swollen throat, alternating fever and chills, fatigue with disinclination to talk, persistent nausea, bitter taste in the mouth, dizziness, possibly tinnitus, irritability, headaches, chest or rib-side pain, fine and thready pulse, and a tongue that is red around the edges with a thin yellow coat.

❖ **Qi Level / Yangming / Taiyin (Spleen-Stomach Axis):**

GI symptoms (abdominal fullness and pain, gnawing appetite, thirst, poor appetite, nausea), spontaneous sweating, shortness of breath, brain fog, food sensitivities, histamine intolerance, low-grade fever (subjective or objective), muscle weakness, loose and/or urgent stools, or constipation.

❖ **Blood Level / Ying Level (Heat in Deeper Tissues):**

Purple skin rashes, cognitive impairment, insomnia, internal heat with dryness, anxiety or disturbances in consciousness, restlessness, tics/tremors, palpitations, menstrual disturbance, fatigue with PEM, spontaneous bleeding (a drop of blood from the nose or other membrane), thin/deep/rapid pulse, and a red/peeled tongue.

❖ **Shaoyin (Heart-Kidney Axis Disruption):**

Insomnia, anxiety, stiff/swollen/achy joints, mouth ulcers, cold intolerance with deep exhaustion and PEM, chronic infections, palpitations, frequent urination, a deep/weak pulse, and a pale tongue with a red tip.

❖ **Jueyin (Heat Above and Cold Below):**

Heat rising with cold below: dizziness, restlessness/confusion, tremors/spasms, cold limbs/feet with flushed face, diarrhea and gut hypersensitivity, extreme fatigue with PEM, a faint pulse, and a very pale/glossy or purple and deeply fissured tongue.

Herbal Treatment Strategy Overview

1. Vent: Open the surface, and restore circulation to blocked or hidden areas. Venting allows internal heat and constraint to release outward, signaling that the pathogen is becoming mobile and accessible to treatment.

2. Protect Qi and Yin: Lingering illness often leaves behind a deficiency. Protecting Qi and Yin prevents further damage during dispersing or clearing therapies and ensures the system has the strength to mount an adequate response.

3. Drain: Use draining strategies, through urination, bowels, or sweat, to remove internal heat, damp, and toxin accumulation. These methods help relieve pressure and move the pathogen out through proper channels.

4. Disperse and Clear: Break up lingering heat, stasis, and phlegm; clear hidden pathogens and inflammatory debris. This phase targets what remains entrenched, while monitoring closely to avoid harming the recovering terrain.

Jun-Chen-Zuo-Shi

Before we move into the more advanced concept of herbal formulas, it's worth revisiting one of the most enduring and elegant principles of Chinese herbal formulation: the Jun-Chen-Zuo-Shi hierarchy. Translated as Emperor, Minister, Assistant, and Envoy, this framework describes the roles herbs play within a formula, where one leads with the primary therapeutic action (Emperor), another supports or broadens that action (Minister), a third moderates side effects or counterbalances (Assistant), and a fourth guides the formula to specific organs or harmonizes the whole (Envoy).

This relational model is not merely a classical artifact; it offers a nuanced, systemic logic for working with complexity, particularly in syndromes like Lingering Pathogenic Illness, where treatment must be layered, adaptable, and often multidimensional. By understanding Jun-Chen-Zuo-Shi, we can approach even modern polyherbal formulations with greater intentionality, seeing them not just as accumulations of ingredients, but as interwoven therapeutic strategies. In that sense, the formulas and their modifications that follow are less a departure from tradition than a modern expression of this core logic.

Wei Level Pattern: Qi Deficiency and Surface Dysregulation

Yu Ping Feng San + Sheng Mai San	Gui Zhi Jia Huang Qi Tang	Shen Su Yin
recurrent colds spontaneous sweating weak pulse hypotension shortness of breath dry mouth	chills and fever sweating neck stiffness weak, floating pulse itchy skin worse with cold	pronounced congestion persistent runny nose cough with phlegm chest oppression frail pulse
Modified Yu Ping Feng San + Sheng Mai San 30g Huang Qi *(Astragalus Membranaceus)* 60g Bai Zhu *(Atractylodis Macrocephalae Rhizoma)* 30g Fang Feng *(Saposhnikoviae Radix)* 15g Ren Shen *(Ginseng Radix)* 12g Mai Men Dong *(Ophiopogonis Radix)* 6g Wu Wei Zi *(Schisandrae Fructus)* +6g Fu Ling *(Poria Cocos)*	Modified Gui Zhi Jia Huang Qi Tang 6g Gui Zhi *(Cinnamomi Radix)* 9g Bai Shao *(Paeoniae Radix)* 9g Sheng Jiang *(Zingiberis Radix)* 12pcs Da Zao *(Jujube Fructus)* 6g Zhi Gan Cao *(Glycyrrhizae Radix Uralensis)* 24g Huang Qi *(Astragalus Membranaceus)* +6g Fu Ling *(Poria Cocos)* +12g Ge Gen *(Puerariae Radix)*	Shen Su Yin 22.5g Ren Shen *(Ginseng Radix)* 22.5g Zi Su Ye *(Perillae Folium)* 22.5g Ge Gen *(Puerariae Radix)* 22.5g Zhi Ban Xia *(Pinelliae Rhizoma Preparatum)* 22.5g Qian Hu *(Peucedani Radix)* 22.5g Fu Ling *(Poria Cocos)* 15g Mu Xiang *(Aucklandiae Radix)* 15g Zhi Ke *(Aurantii Fructus)* 15g Jie Geng *(Platycodi Radix)* 15g Zhi Gan Cao *(Glycyrrhizae Radix Uralensis)*

Shaoyang Level / Membrane Source Pattern: Stagnation and Heat

Qing Pi Tang (variation of Da Yuan Yin)	Xiao Chai Hu Tang	Chai Hu Jia Long Gu Mu Li Tang
more fever than chills distention, gas, loss of appetite thirst, bitter taste in mouth dark urine, constipation rapid/wiry pulse yellow/greasy tongue coat	more fever than chills nausea, food tastes bad hypochondriac pain	more fever than chills agitation, chest oppression irritability, insomnia constipation
Modified Qing Pi Tang 4.5g Qing Pi *(Citri Reticulatae Pericarpium)* 9g Hou Po *(Magnoliae Cortex)* 9g Bai Zhu *(Atractylodis Macrocephalae Rhizoma)* 6g Cao Guo *(Tsaoko Fructus)* 9g Chai Hu *(Bupleuri Radix)* 12g Fu Ling *(Poria Cocos)* 12g Zhi Ban Xia *(Pinelliae Rhizoma Preparatum)* 9g Huang Qin *(Scutellariae Radix)* 3g Zhi Gan Cao *(Glycyrrhizae Radix Uralensis)* +12g Dang Shen *(Codonopsis Radix)* +12g Ge Gen *(Puerariae Radix)* +6g Yu Jin *(Curcumae Radix)*	Modified Xiao Chai Hu Tang 12g Chai Hu *(Bupleuri Radix)* 9g Huang Qin *(Scutellariae Radix)* 24g Zhi Ban Xia *(Pinelliae Rhizoma Preparatum)* ~~9g Ren Shen *(Ginseng Radix)*~~ 9g Zhi Gan Cao *(Glycyrrhizae Radix Uralensis)* 9g Sheng Jiang *(Zingiberis Radix)* 12pcs Da Zao *(Jujube Fructus)* +3g Fu Ling *(Poria Cocos)* +12g Dang Shen *(Codonopsis Radix)*	Modified Chai Hu Jia Long Gu Mu Li Tang 12g Chai Hu *(Bupleuri Radix)* 4.5g Gui Zhi *(Cinnamomi Ramulus)* 6g Da Huang *(Rhei Radix et Rhizoma)* 4.5g Mu Li *(Ostreae Concha)* 4.5g Dai Zhe Shi *(Haematitum)* 4.5g Huang Qin *(Scutellaria Radix)* 4.5g Long Gu *(Fossilia Ossis Mastodi)* 9g Zhi Ban Xia *(Pinelliae Rhizoma Preparatum)* 4.5g Fu Ling *(Poria Cocos)* ~~4.5g Ren Shen *(Ginseng Radix)*~~ 4.5g Sheng Jiang *(Zingiberis Radix)* 6pcs Da Zao *(Jujube Fructus)* +9g Yu Jin *(Curcumae Radix)* +24g Tai Zi Shen*(Pseudostellariae Radix)*

Qi Level / Yangming Pattern: Damp Heat damage to Qi and Yin

Zhu Ye Shi Gao Tang	Ban Xia Xie Xin Tang	Wen Dan Tang
fever sweating thirst forceless pulse	Epigastric fullness Nausea, vomiting, Diarrhea with or without pain rapid/wiry pulse	dizziness, vertigo nausea, vomiting dream disturbed sleep palpitations, anxiety
Modified Zhu Ye Shi Gao Tang 3g Dan Zhu Ye *(Lophatheri Herba)* 12g Shi Gao *(Gypsum Fibrosum)* 3g Ren Shen *(Ginseng Radix)* 12g Mai Men Dong *(Ophiopogonis Radix)* 9g Zhi Ban Xia *(Pinelliae Rhizoma)* 9g Geng Mi *(Oryzae Semen)* 6g Zhi Gan Cao *(Glycyrrhizae Radix Preparatum)* +6g Fu Ling *(Poria Cocos)* +12g Ge Gen *(Puerariae Radix)*	Modified Ban Xia Xie Xin Tang 12g Zhi Ban Xia *(Pinelliae Rhizoma)* 9g Gan Jiang *(Zingiberis Radix)* 9g Huang Qin *(Scutellaria Radix)* 3g Huang Lian *(Coptis Rhizome)* ~~9g Ren Shen *(Ginseng Radix)*~~ 12pcs Da Zao *(Jujube Fructus)* 9g Zhi Gan Cao *(Glycyrrhizae Radix Uralensis)* +3g Fu Ling *(Poria Cocos)* +12g Ge Gen *(Puerariae Radix)* +18g Dang Shen *(Codonopsis Radix)*	Modified Wen Dan Tang 6g Zhi Ban Xia *(Pinelliae Rhizoma)* 6g Zhu Ru *(Bambusae Caulis in Taeniam)* 6g Zhi Shi *(Aurantii Fructus Immaturus)* 9g Chen Pi *(Citri Reticulatae Pericarpium)* 5g Fu Ling *(Poria Cocos)* 5pcs Sheng Jiang *(Zingiberis Radix)* 1pcs Da Zao *(Jujube Fructus)* 3g Gan Cao *(Glycyrrhizae Radix Uralensis)* +12g Dang Shen *(Codonopsis Radix)* +12g Ge Gen *(Puerariae Radix)*

Ying Level / Blood Level: Deep Inflammation, Yin Deficiency

Qing Ying Tang	Qing Hao Bie Jia Tang	Shui Niu Jiao Di Huang
night fever, irritability, restlessness	night fever(no sweating) morning coolness emaciation, Qi level relatively unaffected	Night fever sudden bleeding(nose, other…), thirst, dryness purpura, maculopapular rashes
Modified Qing Ying Tang ~~30g Shui Niu Jiao *(Bubali Cornu)*~~ +45g Sheng Di Huang *(Rehmanniae Radix)* 9g Xuan Shen *(Scrophulariae Radix)* 9g Mai Men Dong *(Ophiopogonis Radix)* 9g Jin Yin Hua *(Lonicerae Flos)* 6g Lian Qiao *(Forsythiae Fructus)* 5g Huang Lian *(Coptidis Rhizoma)* 3g Dan Zhu Ye *(Lophatheri Herba)* 6g Dan Shen *(Salviae Miltiorrhizae Radix* +6g Fu Ling *(Poria Cocos)* +12g Ling Zhi *(Ganoderma)* +12g Ge Gen *(Puerariae Radix)* +6g Yu Jin *(Curcumae Radix)*	Modified Qing Hao Bie Jia Tang 15g Bie Jia *(Trionycis Carapax)* 6g Qing Hao *(Artemisiae Annuae Herba)* 6g Zhi Mu *(Anemarrhenae Rhizoma)* 12g Sheng Di Huang *(Rehmanniae Radix)* 9g Mu Dan Pi *(Moutan Cortex)* +24g Ling Zhi *(Ganoderma)* +3g Fu Ling *(Poria Cocos)* +12g Ge Gen *(Puerariae Radix)*	Modified Shui Niu Jiao Di Huang ~~30g Shui Niu Jiao *(Bubali Cornu)*~~ +60g Sheng Di Huang *(Rehmanniae Radix)* ~~12g Chi Shao *(Paeoniae Radix Rubra)*~~ 12g Mu Dan Pi *(Moutan Cortex)* +12g Ge Gen *(Puerariae Radix)* +24 Ling Zhi *(Ganoderma)* +6g Fu Ling *(Poria Cocos)* +6g Yu Jin *(Curcumae Radix)*

Shaoyin Channel / Lesser Yin: Heat Transformation, Cold Transformation

Shen Qi Wan	Tian Wang Bu Xin Dan	Huang Lian E Jiao Tang
Cold Transformation, achy/swollen joints, frequent urination	Heat Transformation, Heart-Kidney disconnection, Insomnia, nightsweats, anxiety, palpitations, mouth sores, facial flushing, red dry tongue	Heat Transformation, Insomnia anxiety, palpitations, restlessness, mouth sores
Modified Shen Qi Wan 3g Zhi Fu Zi *(Aconiti Radix Lateralis* 3g Gui Zhi *(Cinnamomi Ramulus)* 24g Sheng Di *(Rehmanniae Radix)* 12g Shan Zhu Yu *(Corni Fructus)* 12g Shan Yao *(Dioscoreae Rhizoma)* 9g Ze Xie *(Alismatis Rhizoma)* 9g Fu Ling *(Poria Cocos)* 9g Mu Dan Pi *(Moutan Cortex)* +3g Che Qian Zi *(Plantaginis Semen)* +6g Ge Gen *(Puerariae Radix)* +12g Tai Zi Shen *(Pseudostellariae Radix)*	Modified Tian Wang Bu Xin Dan 120g Sheng Di Huang *(Rehmanniae Radix)* 15g Ren Shen *(Ginseng Radix)* 30g Tian Men Dong *(Asparagi Radix)* 30g Mai Men Dong *(Ophiopogonis Radix)* 15g Dan Shen *(Salviae Miltiorrhizae Radix)* 15g Fu Ling *(Poria Cocos)* 30g Dang Gui *(Angelicae Sinensis Radix)* 15g Xuan Shen *(Scrophulariae Radix)* 15g Yuan Zhi *(Polygalae Radix)* 30g Wu Wei Zi *(Schisandrae Fructus)* 30g Bai Zi Ren *(Platycladi Semen)* 30g Suan Zao Ren *(Jujube Semen)* 15g Zhu Sha *(Cinnabaris)* 15g Jie Geng *(Platycodi Radix)* +15g Ling Zhi *(Ganoderma)* +15g Ge Gen *(Puerariae Radix)*	Modified Huang Lian E Jiao Tang 12g Huang Lian *(Coptidis Rhizoma)* 9g E Jiao *(Asini Corii Colla)* 6g Huang Qin *(Scutellariae Radix)* 6g Shao Yao *(Paeoniae Radix)* ~~2 yolks Ji Zi Huang *(Gallus Domesticus Braisson)*~~ +12g Tai Zi Shen *(Pseudostellariae Radix)* +6g Fu Ling *(Poria Cocos)* +6g Ge Gen *(Puerariae Radix)* +6g Dan Shen *(Salviae Miltiorrhizae Radix)*

Jueyin Channel / Terminal Layer Pathology: Cold Below, Heat Above

Wu Mei Wan
cold extremities, diarrhea, abdominal pain relieved by warmth
Modified Wu Mei Wan 30g Wu Mei *(Mume Fructus)* 6g Hua Jiao *(Zanthoxyli Pericarpium)* ~~3g Xi Xin *(Asari Radix et Rhizoma)*~~ 6g Huang Lian *(Coptidis Rhizoma)* 6g Huang Bai *(Phellodendri Cortex)* 6g Zhi Fu Zi *(Aconiti Radix Lateralis Preparata)* 6g Gui Zhi *(Cinnamomi Ramulus)* 9g Gan Jiang *(Zingiberis Radix)* 6g Ren Shen *(Ginseng Radix)* 6g Dang Gui *(Angelicae Sinensis Radix)* +12g Sheng Di Huang *(Rehmanniae Radix)* +6g Fu Ling *(Poria Cocos)*

Blood Level Stasis with Heat and Qi Deficiency

Xue Fu Zhu Yu Tang	Tao Hong Si Wu Tang
Qi stagnation with Blood Stasis, pain in the chest, headache	Blood deficiency with Blood Stasis, gynecological issues
Modified Xue Fu Zhu Yu Tang	Modified Tao Hong Si Wu Tang
12g Tao Ren *(Persicae Semen)*	15g Shu Di Huang *(Rehmanniae Radix Preparata)*
9g Hong Hua *(Carthami Flos)*	12g Dang Gui *(Angelicae Sinensis Radix)*
5g Chuan Xiong *(Chuanxiong Rhizoma)*	10g Bai Shao *(Paeoniae Radix)*
~~6g Chi Shao *(Paeoniae Radix Rubra)*~~	8g Chuan Xiong *(Chuanxiong Rhizoma)*
9g Dang Gui *(Angelicae Sinensis Radix)*	6g Tao Ren *(Persicae Semen)*
9g Sheng Di Huang *(Rehmanniae Radix)*	4g Hong Hua *(Carthami Flos)*
9g Niu Xi *(Achyranthis Bidentatae Radix)*	+24g Dang Shen *(Codonopsis Radix)*
3g Chai Hu *(Bupleuri Radix)*	+6g Fu Ling *(Poria Cocos)*
5g Jie Geng *(Platycodi Radix)*	
6g Zhi Ke *(Aurantii Fructus)*	
3g Gan Cao *(Glycyrrhizae Radix)*	
+24g Dang Shen *(Codonopsis Radix)*	
+6g Fu Ling *(Poria Cocos)*	
+6g Yu Jin *(Curcumae Radix)*	
Modifications: Add Su Ma + Dan Shen for mild cases; Pu Huang + Shui Zhi for severe cases[211]	

[211] Yan De-xin. *Aging and Blood Stasis: A New TCM Approach to Geriatrics*. Translated by Philip Sinnott. Paradigm Publications, 2004

Lingering Pathogenic Illness Support Guide

LPI describes an injury to the immune system from which the patient fails to recover. It may present as a persistent or relapsing infection, though it's not always microbe-specific.

The concept of lingering pathogens dates back over 4,000 years to the *Huang Di Nei Jing Su Wen*, *Shang Han Lun*, and *Wen Re Lun*, later refined by Lei Feng and Liu Bao-Yi.

Modern parallels include chronic viral, bacterial, protozoal, or fungal infections, CFS/ME, Long Covid, Post-Vaccination Syndrome, food intolerances, environmental toxicities, and chronic inflammatory or autoimmune diseases.

Treatment relies primarily on herbal medicine (with acupuncture aiding venting at the Qi and Shaoyang levels) to tonify Qi and Yin while promoting Qi functions—opening pores, supporting elimination, and clearing heat with salty, pungent, and sweet herbs. Caution: Cold/bitter medicinals may drive pathogens deeper.

Wei Level:	Qi Level:	Shaoyang:	Ying/Blood:	Shaoyin:	Jueyin:
floating pulse swollen glands clammy skin Itchy skin runny nose nasal congestion fatigue	low grade fever dryness, thirst sweating fatigue swollen glands muscle/joint aching/weakness insomnia restlessness/irritability dry/peeled tongue coat Thick tongue coat mucous/serous discharge Vesicular skin lesions →	alternating fever/chills swollen glands fatigue dizziness nausea loss of appetite temporal headache TMJ lesions on sides of body →	recurrent low grade fever at night dryness fatigue and exhaustion swollen glands red or crimson dry tongue, no coat skin rashes →	lower back ache urinary dysfunction tinnitus, hearing loss joint swelling/pain →	thirst flushing restlessness and confusion tremors and spasms vertigo frequent urination / diarrhea cold legs and feet →

*Over time, lingering pathogens progress deeper into the body

Wei Level:	Qi Level:	Shaoyang:	Ying/Blood:	Shaoyin:	Jueyin:
Ying/Wei dysharmony: ***Gui Zhi Jia Huang Qi Tang*** (Additional symptoms: Itchy skin lesions, sweating worse with Cold) Cold Invasion/Qi deficiency: ***Shen Su Yin*** (Additional symptoms: Persistent runny nose) Qi/Wei Insufficiency: ***Yu Ping Feng San*** + ***Sheng Mai San*** (Additional symptoms: weak pulse, hypotension recurrent colds, sweating shortness of breath dry mouth)	Lung Heat/Qi and Fluid Damage: ***Zhu Ye Shi Gao Tang*** (Additional symptoms: dry hacking cough worse at night, nausea vomiting, hunger) Heat AND Cold in Stomach ***Ban Xia Xie Xin Tang*** (Additional symptoms: epigastric fullness, acid reflux nausea, belching, diarrhea) Phlegm Heat: ***Wen Dan Tang*** (Additional symptoms: fatigue, anxiety, palpitations insomnia, dizziness, nausea)	Heat: ***Xiao Chai Hu Tang*** (Additional symptoms: more fever than chills, food tastes bad, hypochondriac pain) Phlegm/Damp Heat: ***Qing Pi Tang*** (Additional symptoms: distention, fever/chills thirst, bitter taste, constipation, dark urine, greasy/yellow tongue coat) +Taiyang: ***Chai Hu Gui Zhi Tang*** (Additional symptoms: more chills than fever, joint/muscle aches, creaking joints) Taiyang/Yangming/Shaoyang: ***Chai Hu Jia Long Gu Mu Li Tang*** (Additional Symptoms: constipation, agitation, chest distention, insomnia, palpitations, heaviness in entire body)	Ying/Blood: ***Qing Ying Tang*** (Additional symptoms: joint pain/inflammation, vasculitis, mouth ulcers, insomnia, weight loss, skin rashes(flare at night) Blood: ***Qing Hao Bie Jia Tang*** (Additional symptoms: night fever(no sweating), morning coolness, emaciation, Qi level relatively unaffected) Blood: ***Shui Niu Jiao Di Huang*** (Additional symptoms: night fever, sudden bleeding, thirst, dryness, purpura, maculopapular rashes)	Heat Transformation: ***Tian Wang Bu Xin Dan*** (Additional symptoms: facial flushing, night sweats, dysuria insomnia, anxiety, palpitations, joint inflammation, red dry tongue) Cold Transformation: ***Jin Gui Shen Qi Wan*** (Additional symptoms: cold intolerance, urinary frequency, nocturia or edema and oliguria, stiff swollen aching joints, pale swollen tongue) Heat Transformation: ***Huang Lian E Jiao Tang*** (Additional symptoms: insomnia, anxiety, restlessness palpitations, mouth sores)	Cold below / Heat above ***Wu Mei Wan*** (Additional symptoms: thirst, flushing, restlessness and confusion, muscle spasms and tremor, vertigo, frequent urination and diarrhea, cold legs and feet) **Blood Stasis:** Blood Stasis / Qi Stagnation: ***Xue Fu Zhu Yu Tang*** (Additional symptoms: pain in the chest, headache) Blood Deficiency/Stasis: ***Tao Hong Si Wu Tang*** (Additional symptoms: gynecological issues)

Modern Considerations for Lingering Pathogenic Illnesses:

The formulas above fall short in treating Lingering Pathogenic Illness because many contain herbs that impair antigen-presenting cells (APCs) - an immune subset damaged in LPI. To restore Qi, Yin, and APC function, these formulas should be modified with the following herbs (or similar):

Bai Zhu	Lu Hui
Che Qian Zi	Mai Men Dong
Dang Shen	Neem
Fang Feng	Niu Xi
Fu Ling	Ren Sheng
Ge Gen	Rou Cong Rong
Gou Teng	Sang Ji Sheng
Hu Zhang	Shan Yao
Huang Jing	Sheng Di Huang
Huang Qi	Tai Zi Shen
Jie Geng	Zhi Ban Xia
Ku Shen	Zhi Gan Cao
Ling Zhi	

How to tell if a Lingering Pathogenic Illness is Resolving:

Patient should experience a reverse channel progression of symptoms notably with

- low-grade fever or subjective heat
- exacerbation of fatigue, brain fog
- swollen lymph nodes, sore throat
- spontaneous sweating, itching, rashes
- dizziness, irritability, restlessness
- thirst, nausea, bloating, dark yellow urine
- Red and/or burning tongue tip
- muscle/joint aches, palpitations
- loose stools, mild cramping

Patient should be encouraged to continue treatment despite discomfort until symptoms resolve.

Chapter 7: APC Restore a Foundational Formula for Immune Realignment

In this chapter, we'll explore my APC Restore formula for Lingering Pathogenic Illness, an alternative approach that can be used independently or alongside the classical pattern-based formulations discussed in Chapter 6.

As clinical understanding deepens, a need has emerged for a formula that provides foundational recalibration, one that corrects the core bioenergetic and immunologic discrepancies common to most LPI phenotypes. This formula, APC Restore, is meant to be combined with pattern-specific formulas to optimize their effects.

APC Restore embodies the integration of modern immunometabolic science with classical Chinese medical principles. Designed to reestablish antigen-presenting cell competence, it addresses the metabolic bottlenecks underlying immune exhaustion - such as succinate accumulation, oxidative stress, and tricarboxylic acid(TCA) cycle[212] disruption - while enhancing microcirculatory flow and redox balance[213].

---

[212] TCA Cycle: The tricarboxylic acid (TCA) cycle - also known as the Krebs or citric acid cycle - is a central metabolic pathway that takes place in the mitochondrial matrix, converting acetyl-CoA derived from carbohydrates, fats, and amino acids into ATP, NADH, and $FADH_2$ for cellular energy production. Beyond its role in bioenergetics, the TCA cycle provides intermediates for amino acid synthesis, redox balance, and immune cell metabolism. Disruptions in TCA flux are characteristic of chronic inflammation and immune exhaustion, where mitochondrial dysfunction limits ATP generation and shifts metabolism toward glycolysis or incomplete oxidation. In immune regulation, proper TCA cycling supports antigen presentation, cytokine signaling, and resolution of inflammation. In Chinese medicine terms, the TCA cycle mirrors the continuous transformation of Qi and Yang - governing metabolic warmth, movement, and vitality - while its failure reflects Qi deficiency and metabolic stagnation.

[213] Redox Balance: The dynamic equilibrium between oxidation and reduction reactions that governs cellular energy flow, metabolic signaling, and oxidative stress. In physiological conditions, reactive oxygen and nitrogen species are balanced by antioxidant systems such as glutathione and superoxide dismutase, maintaining proper immune and mitochondrial function. When this balance is lost - through excess oxidant production or insufficient antioxidant capacity - oxidative stress arises, damaging cellular structures and impairing immune regulation. In chronic inflammatory or infectious states, persistent redox imbalance contributes to antigen-presenting cell exhaustion, mitochondrial dysfunction, and impaired recovery. In Chinese medicine terms, redox balance parallels the dynamic interplay of Fire (oxidative drive, metabolic activity) and Water (Yin containment, antioxidant capacity), reflecting the harmonious transformation of Qi and preservation of Yin.

Key nutrients like magnesium aspartate, taurine, dihydroberberine, and liposomal glutathione restore mitochondrial integrity and metabolic tone, while Ling Zhi, Huang Qi, Bai Zhu, and Gou Teng recalibrate immune signaling and fortify the constitutional strength of Qi and Blood. Complementary support from trace minerals, zinc, and lumbrokinase improves vascular perfusion and nutrient delivery, ensuring that cellular recovery unfolds within a balanced metabolic and energetic framework.

This chapter will explain the immunologic rationale for each ingredient, describe the dosing and implementation strategy, and guide practitioners and patients through the clinical logic behind this deep, terrain-based formula.

The Pathophysiology of Lingering Metabolic Inflammation

At the core of Lingering Pathogenic Illness lies a metabolic-immune stalemate - a condition in which cellular energy systems and immune recognition remain locked in a defensive posture long after the original trigger has passed. This persistence is sustained not by active infection but by maladaptive feedback between redox imbalance, microvascular stasis, and immune exhaustion. What begins as a protective metabolic shift gradually evolves into a state of bioenergetic isolation, marked by mitochondrial dysfunction, tissue hypoxia, and antigen-presenting cell (APC) dysfunction.

Redox Imbalance and Mineral Depletion

Chronic immune activation rapidly consumes essential cofactors such as zinc, selenium, and magnesium - trace minerals that anchor antioxidant enzymes and maintain mitochondrial stability. Their depletion weakens superoxide dismutase and glutathione peroxidase activity, causing oxidative stress and impaired NAD+/NADH cycling. As redox balance collapses, cells revert to glycolysis despite oxygen availability - a pseudo-hypoxic, energy-inefficient state that sustains inflammation and prevents immune resolution.

The Itaconate Shunt: A Protective Detour Turned Pathologic

Within APCs, redox imbalance converges with activation of the itaconate shunt, an immune-driven rerouting of the TCA cycle. Under TLR and interferon signaling, the enzyme IRG1 converts citrate into itaconate, which inhibits succinate dehydrogenase (SDH), halting both the TCA cycle and complex II of the electron transport chain. This mechanism limits pathogen access to host energy but, when prolonged, traps immune cells in a state of metabolic dormancy - unable to complete oxidative phosphorylation or regenerate NAD+, leaving them reactive but directionless.

Succinate and the Persistence of Inflammation

Inhibition of SDH leads to accumulation of succinate, which acts as a signaling molecule rather than a benign metabolite. Elevated succinate stabilizes HIF-1α, amplifying IL-1β and TNF-α production while suppressing regulatory T-cell (Treg) formation. The result is sustained inflammation without resolution. This same dysregulation extends to the vasculature, where oxidative stress and endothelial activation promote fibrin deposition and microclot formation - further restricting oxygen delivery and deepening cellular hypoxia.

Microvascular Stasis and Immune Isolation

Fibrin buildup and endothelial irritation create pockets of metabolic congestion, where nutrients, oxygen, and cytokine signals cannot circulate freely. This vascular stagnation sustains fatigue, cognitive fog, and autonomic instability. Enzymatic fibrinolytics such as lumbrokinase help break this pattern by clearing fibrin, improving capillary flow, and reopening the physiological “channels” that allow immune signaling.

APC Exhaustion: The Immune Blind Spot

In this terrain, dendritic cells and macrophages become metabolically starved and immunologically muted. MHC expression declines, co-stimulatory molecules such as CD80 and CD86 are downregulated, and Fcγ receptor signaling skews toward chronic irritation rather than tolerance. The immune system remains vigilant but disoriented - perpetually alert, yet unable to reset.

Restoring Coherence: The Metabolic Path to Resolution

Reversing this loop requires reestablishing metabolic coherence, not merely dampening inflammation. Magnesium aspartate revives the malate-aspartate shuttle to restore NAD+ balance; dihydroberberine activates AMPK, reducing glycolytic entrapment; liposomal glutathione reconstitutes antioxidant capacity; taurine stabilizes cellular membranes and calcium signaling; and Ling Zhi with Huang Qi rebuilds mitochondrial and immunological tone.

Together, these mechanisms reopen communication between energy metabolism and immune function - enabling APCs to perceive, respond, and ultimately resolve. This is the central therapeutic goal of APC Restore: to transform a static, defensive metabolism into one capable of regeneration and clarity.

Mechanisms and Functions of APC Restore

Trace Mineral Blend (600 mg):

Essential microelements such as zinc, selenium, manganese, and molybdenum act as cofactors for redox enzymes and mitochondrial complexes. These trace minerals restore enzymatic function within antioxidant systems (superoxide dismutase, glutathione peroxidase) and support DNA repair, protein folding, and immune cell signaling. In antigen-presenting cells (APCs), adequate trace mineral status is critical for MHC expression, cytokine modulation, and metabolic flexibility under inflammatory stress. Clinically, replenishment of trace minerals enhances recovery from redox exhaustion, supports connective tissue integrity, and stabilizes neuroendocrine tone.

Liposomal Zinc (25 mg):

Zinc is vital for immune cell differentiation, antiviral defense, and membrane stabilization. Its liposomal delivery enhances bioavailability and intracellular penetration, supporting thymic output and reducing inflammatory cytokine expression. Zinc also modulates the activity of metalloproteinases and protects against oxidative damage to mitochondrial and nuclear DNA. Within APCs, zinc is required for antigen processing and the regulation of TLR4 and NF-κB signaling.

Clinically, supplementation may reduce neuroinflammation, restore mucosal immunity, and prevent viral reactivation during recovery phases.

Magnesium Aspartate (300 mg):

Magnesium supports ATP synthesis, NMDA receptor stability, and cellular redox buffering, while aspartate feeds the malate-aspartate shuttle to restore mitochondrial NAD+/NADH cycling. This pairing helps maintain energy throughput in immune-stressed mitochondria and supports cardiac and neuromuscular equilibrium. Clinically, it alleviates fatigue, muscle tightness, and post-exertional malaise, while stabilizing metabolic rhythm during detoxification and repair.

Lumbrokinase (200 mg):

A fibrinolytic enzyme complex derived from earthworms, lumbrokinase breaks down fibrin deposits that accumulate after endothelial injury and immune activation. By reducing microclots and hyperviscosity, it improves tissue oxygenation, lymphatic flow, and the delivery of immune signals to isolated compartments. In chronic inflammatory syndromes characterized by fibrin-mediated immune sequestration, lumbrokinase promotes recirculation of metabolic and immune resources, aiding detoxification and reducing vascular inflammation.

Taurine (700 mg):

A sulfur-containing amino acid and cellular osmolyte, taurine stabilizes mitochondrial membranes, regulates intracellular calcium, and supports the detoxification of reactive aldehydes and bile acids. It modulates the GABAergic system and suppresses microglial hyperactivation, reducing excitotoxicity and neuroinflammation. Taurine also buffers oxidative stress in endothelial and immune cells, enhancing tolerance and preventing flare responses. Clinically, it supports orthostatic stability, emotional calm, and cellular recovery following exertion or immune surges.

Dihydroberberine (150 mg):

A highly bioavailable form of berberine, dihydroberberine modulates AMPK activation, improves glucose metabolism, and corrects microbiome-derived metabolic endotoxemia. It inhibits NF-κB and MAPK signaling while enhancing mitochondrial biogenesis and insulin sensitivity. In APCs, dihydroberberine supports balanced cytokine output and reduces succinate accumulation, mitigating inflammatory mitochondrial stalling. Clinically, it aids gut-immune recalibration, reduces postprandial crashes, and supports the microbiome's metabolic ecology.

Liposomal Glutathione (400 mg):

The master intracellular antioxidant, glutathione regulates redox signaling, maintains thiol balance, and detoxifies peroxides, xenobiotics, and heavy metals. The liposomal form bypasses gastrointestinal degradation, enhancing cellular uptake. In APCs, glutathione prevents oxidative inactivation of surface receptors and supports antigen presentation fidelity. Clinically, it reduces hypersensitivity, chemical intolerance, and inflammatory fatigue while supporting cognitive clarity and hepatic detoxification.

Ling Zhi / Gou Teng (500 mg):

- ❖ **Ling Zhi (Ganodernum):** enhances mitochondrial function and immune regulation through its triterpenoids and polysaccharides. It modulates the gut-brain axis, promotes Treg balance, and attenuates neuroinflammation. In the context of APC restoration, Ling Zhi supports immunological tolerance, oxygen utilization, and cellular resilience during redox stress. Clinically, it calms inflammatory agitation, stabilizes sleep, and restores adaptive immune rhythm.

- ❖ **Gou Teng (Uncaria):** complements Ling Zhi by relaxing vascular tone, dispersing latent heat, and easing neurologic excitability. Together, they regulate the neuroimmune interface, protect endothelial and glial networks, and guide antigen-presenting cells toward balanced, responsive activity.

Wu Wei Zi / Shan Zha / Huang Qi (600 mg):

- **Wu Wei Zi (Schisandra):** Tonifies Essence, preserves adaptive reserves, and protects hepatic detoxification pathways.

- **Shan Zha (Crataegus):** Enhances coronary and cerebral circulation, promotes metabolic clearance of lipids and metabolites, and relieves digestive stagnation common in immune-overloaded states.

- **Huang Qi (Astragalus):** Strengthens Wei Qi, supports mucosal immunity, and promotes macrophage and dendritic cell recovery after depletion.

Bai Zhu / Fu Ling / Wu Wei Zi / Fang Feng (275 mg):

- **Bai Zhu (Atractylodes):** Tonifies Spleen Qi, preventing Damp accumulation and improving metabolic clarity.

- **Fu Ling (Poria):** Strengthens the middle burner, supports lymphatic drainage, and calms the spirit.

- **Neem (Azadirachta Indica):** clears latent heat and microbial residues, promotes antigen processing, and refines immune vigilance without overstimulation.

- **Fang Feng (Saposhnikovia):** Expels residual pathogens and modulates mast cell activity.

APC Restore (one dose)
925mg Multi-mineral Blend 200mg Lumbrokinase 700mg Taurine 150mg Dihydroberberine *(Berberinum)* 400mg Liposomal Glutathione 250mg Ling Zhi *(Ganoderma)* 250mg Gou Teng *(Uncaria Ramulus Cum Uncis)* 200mg Wu Wei Zi *(Schisandrae Fructus)* 200mg Shan Zha *(Crataegii Fructus)* 200mg Huang Qi *(Astragali Radix)* 69mg Bai Zhu *(Atractylodis Macrocephalae Radix)* 69mg Fu Ling *(Poria Cocos* 69mg Neem *(Azadirachta indica)* 69mg Fang Feng *(Saposhnikoviae Radix)*

Acupuncture Protocol for Lingering Pathogenic Illness

Lingering Pathogenic Illness often leaves the body in a state of deep imbalance, pathogens lodged beyond the reach of the Wei Qi, organ systems taxed by prolonged inflammation, and circulation impaired at both the primary and extraordinary channel levels. This protocol addresses both the organ-specific dysfunction and the systemic stagnation that allow the illness to persist.

Point Selection and Rationale

1. UB17 - Geshu (Influential Point of Blood): Provides a global regulation of systemic circulation and Blood transformation. UB17 harmonizes the diaphragm and supports the movement of Qi and Blood through all Zang-Fu, making it particularly suited for conditions of lingering pathogen and post-inflammatory stasis. It clears residual heat, nourishes Blood, and facilitates oxygenation and metabolic recovery. In chronic infectious or inflammatory conditions, UB17 restores the interface between respiration and Blood, addressing both hypoxia and immune stagnation.

2. SP21 - Great Luo of the Spleen: Opens the Great Luo, which connects and influences all Luo vessels, mirroring the Chong Mai in global Qi and Blood distribution via the Qi of the chest. Especially indicated for generalized body pain, heaviness, and fatigue. Restores systemic circulation and unblocks stagnation in the chronic phase.

3. LV13 - Front-Mu of Spleen / Hui of Zang: Regulates Liver–Spleen interaction and resonates with the Dai Mai, the extraordinary vessel that "binds" the body's pivot. This helps release pathogens, trauma, and repressed emotions/memories bound in the trunk. It also harmonizes digestive-immune function, a critical axis in post-viral recovery.

4. UB43 - Gao Huang Shu: Deeply tonifies the Lungs, Heart, Spleen, Kidneys, Stomach, and constitutional Qi. Used for chronic depletion and to support immune resilience. In modern applications, it is one of the most effective points for post-viral illness.

5. Ren 4 - Guanyuan *(with moxibustion):* A key point for nourishing Yuan Qi, warming deficiency cold, and strengthening both the Kidneys and overall constitutional energy. In LPI, Ren 4 moxa supports recovery from profound depletion.

6. ST 36 - Zusanli *(with moxibustion):* Strengthens Spleen and Stomach Qi, promotes Blood production, supports immune modulation, and enhances recovery. When combined with moxa, it boosts vitality and counteracts lingering fatigue.

Treatment Logic

This combination reaches both primary channels and extraordinary vessels, providing a dual action:

- Restoring systemic circulation to flush residual pathogenic factors.
- Rebalancing organ systems to prevent relapse and rebuild resilience.

In LPI, depth and stagnation are the primary concerns. This protocol works by clearing both simultaneously - reinvigorating Blood movement via UB17 while restoring constitutional Qi through SP21, UB43, Ren 4, and ST36.

Chapter 8: Case Studies

Now that we've explored both classical and modern herbal interventions for Lingering Pathogenic Illness, we'll see how these approaches come to life in the following six case studies.

Case 1

One of the more illustrative cases I've encountered involves a 31-year-old elementary school teacher who had been acutely ill on and off for over eight months. Her primary symptoms, persistent sinus congestion, frontal headaches, and crushing fatigue, never fully resolved between flare-ups. She had been prescribed antibiotics five separate times over a five-month span, each round offering diminishing returns. Her primary care physician believed the problem was allergic in nature. The patient, however, suspected something more insidious: mold exposure both in her apartment and in her classroom.

Her case presented initially as a classic Taiyang and Wei Qi level disruption: superficial respiratory symptoms, tension headaches, and immune dysregulation that never quite cleared. I began with a 20-day round of APC Restore, a formula designed to stimulate antigen-presenting cell function, and paired it with Nutricillin by Ecological Formulas, a lactoferrin-based antimicrobial. Within two weeks, her acute symptoms dramatically improved. Sinus inflammation receded, her energy began to return, and for the first time in months, she felt functional.

But, as is often the case with Lingering Pathogenic Illness, removal of the surface layer revealed a deeper stratum of disease. New symptoms emerged: canker sores, nighttime restlessness, and insomnia. These were not random; they reflected a shift into Shaoyin pathology, where depletion and internal heat coexist, especially under emotional stress. At the same time that her symptoms changed, her external situation worsened: her landlord issued an eviction notice, adding anxiety and instability to an already fragile system.

This case demonstrates one of the cardinal dynamics of Lingering Pathogenic Illness: as Wei Qi is restored and surface heat resolves, deeper layers of pathology often emerge, particularly in individuals whose constitutional terrain has been strained for a prolonged period. Shaoyin is especially vulnerable in cases marked by depletion, overwork, emotional distress, and immune exhaustion.

I prescribed Tian Wang Bu Xin Dan to anchor the Heart and Kidney while calming Shen(Spirit), alongside a custom sleep formula designed to support rest and suppress latent heat in the Heart channel. We continued a second round of APC Restore, now with a deeper objective, supporting resolution of residual pathogenic load at the Shaoyin level.

Once stabilized, I advised the patient to take Huang Qi (Astragalus) daily to help maintain a healthy immune tone and restore long-term Wei Qi regulation. She is also taking proactive steps to address the environmental root of her illness: her classroom is being tested for mold, and she is in the process of securing an apartment with healthier living conditions. These external shifts are no less important than the internal ones; they reflect her capacity to protect herself, advocate for care, and shift the terrain in which recovery unfolds.

This case encapsulates a common sequence: Taiyang/Wei dysfunction masked a deeper Shaoyin pathology, only revealed after surface resolution. It also underscores the importance of tracking symptom *transformation* rather than disappearance. In lingering disease, change itself is progress, as long as we remain attentive to the trajectory and depth of each shift.

Herbs for Better Sleep
33g Suan Zao Ren *(Jujube Semen)* 30g Sheng Di Huang *(Rehmanniae Radix)* 15g Long Yan Rou *(Longan Arillus)* 8g Wu Wei Zi *(Schisandrae Fructus)* 5g Bai Shao *(Paeoniae Radix)* 5g Dang Gui *(Angelicae Sinensis Radix)* 3g Bai Zi Ren *(Platycladi Semen)* 3g Dan Dou Chi *(Sojae Semen Preparata)* 3g Dang Shen *(Codonopsis Radix)*

3g Fu Shen *(Poria Sclerotium Pararadicis)*

2g Zhi Zi *(Gardeniae Fructus)*

2g Yuan Zhi *(Polygalae Radix)*

2g Da Zao *(Jujube Fructus)*

2g Huang Bai *(Phellodendri Cortex)*

2g Zhi Mu *(Anemarrhenae Radix)*

1g Mu Xiang *(Aucklandiae Radix)*

Case 2

Another patient, a 38-year-old woman, had lived with Myalgic Encephalomyelitis (ME) for as long as she could remember. Without consistent access to insurance or primary care, she had only received scattered diagnoses over the years: fibromyalgia, PMDD, and little else. Her symptoms had long outpaced the recognition they were given.

Her chief complaint was both acute and disruptive: she had been vomiting every night for several weeks. But this was layered atop a long-standing baseline of full-body pain (especially tender to the touch), post-exertional malaise, joint stiffness, persistent headaches, dizziness, chronic nausea, and aversion to both heat and cold. Her system fluctuated wildly.

Her TCM diagnosis reflected a Liver attacking Spleen pattern compounded by long-term Damp-Heat retention. The core constitutional weakness, Spleen Qi deficiency, had allowed dampness to accumulate, which in time had transformed into Heat. Her heat, however, wasn't blazing on the surface; it was concealed, buried under layers of cold and stasis, a pattern commonly seen in patients with long-duration ME/CFS and Lingering Pathogenic Illness in the Jueyin channel. The surface symptoms, cold sensitivity, pain, and vomiting didn't match a typical febrile pattern, but beneath them, heat smoldered in the Jueyin.

The dual nature of her symptoms, oscillating between stagnation and inflammatory activation, pointed toward a Qi level and Shaoyang pathology, with progression into Shaoyin or Jueyin levels over time. Her body was caught in a state of contradiction: drained and inflamed, sluggish and reactive, weak and easily overwhelmed.

I initiated treatment with Wu Mei Wan, a classical formula for Jueyin/Shaoyin Level illness with heat above and cold below. The choice was rooted in her particular combination of vomiting and dizziness with a deep, wiry pulse, as opposed to a more superficial, slippery pulse that might be seen in a Qi Level presentation. After initiating the formula, her vomiting stopped entirely, her dizziness subsided, and she reported a modest lift in overall body pain.

After this initial resolution, I transitioned her to a modified Shen Qi Wan (see previous chapter) to support her general immune tone, encouraging her to reserve the Wu Mei-based formula for flare-ups or return of Jueyin symptoms. This two-phase strategy, resolving Jueyin heat above and cold below, and then supporting upright Qi, is essential in patients whose Lingering Pathogenic Illness spans both extreme dysharmony and deep deficiency.

Later in our conversation, she shared something critical: her symptoms markedly improved when she was visiting family out of town. This immediately raised the question of mold exposure. I offered education about mold intolerance, its connection to ME symptom flares, and the role of biotoxin accumulation in deep channel pathology. I encouraged her to explore environmental testing and remediation, and to consider moving if and when it becomes feasible.

Her case represents another common arc in Lingering Pathogenic Illness, not an acute trigger followed by decline, but a slow-burning progression over years, shaped by poverty, lack of access to care, and environmental toxicity. The illness was not one event but an accumulation of strain, and her healing will require not only biomedical intervention but the restoration of safe terrain, internal and external.

Case 3

A 72-year-old woman came into the clinic seeking relief from Long Covid symptoms that had become unbearable. She had undergone three heart valve replacements over a decade prior to the pandemic and had been living with the constraints of cardiac medications ever since. One of her persistent complaints was that statins seemed to erase her personality, a deep and unsettling side effect that she had difficulty conveying to her providers.

Before Long Covid, she had adapted to her limitations. But since her SARS-CoV-2 infection, she reported a sharp and debilitating worsening of symptoms: joint pain, muscle pain, unrelenting fatigue, post-exertional malaise, and a cognitive haze that left her in tears. "It's like I'm not here anymore," she told me, describing the depth of disconnection she felt from her body and mind.

She asked to begin with acupuncture, having had some success with it for musculoskeletal pain in the past. But to her surprise, this time the results were faint, barely perceptible. Her system, it seemed, was too depleted and burdened to respond to external stimulation. The Wei Qi layer may have been too compromised to move even small amounts of stagnation without deeper nourishment.

So, we shifted to internal treatment. I designed a custom formula combining elements of Bu Zhong Yi Qi Tang (to support Spleen Qi and lifting function), Er Chen Tang (to resolve dampness and turbidity), and Xue Fu Zhu Yu Tang (to resolve Blood stasis). To support her cardiovascular system, I included essential minerals and taurine, and to gently move blood without overstimulation, I added Dan Shen and Shan Zha. Given her intense cognitive symptoms, I also included Huperzine A, a compound known for its neuroprotective effects and ability to modulate acetylcholine metabolism, which often improves alertness and reduces brain fog in neuroinflammatory conditions.

The transformation was remarkable. Within a week, she returned to say it was the best she had felt in years, not just since Covid. Her energy was back. Her pain had retreated. Her mind had cleared. And in a surprise bonus, she noted that for the first time in memory, her bowels were moving regularly, relieving her of a lifetime of constipation.

With her energy restored and her internal environment more stable, I was then able to reintroduce acupuncture, this time with better results. Her residual aches and discomforts responded quickly now that her system had resources to mobilize.

This case is instructive in multiple ways. First, it underscores how post-viral syndromes can augment pre-existing fragilities, especially in older patients with a history of cardiovascular disease. Second, it demonstrates how acupuncture alone may be insufficient in deep post-viral depletion, especially when the patient is constitutionally drained. And third, it shows how even a simple herbal approach, when attuned to the patient's channels, constitution, and lived history, can shift the entire clinical picture.

Most of all, this case reminds us that regulation precedes repair. Her pain was not an isolated symptom; it was the downstream effect of systemic deficiency, turbidity, and internal stagnation. Once the core was nourished and cleared, the periphery followed.

Case 4

A 31-year-old trans man sought treatment for post-Covid restricted breathing and chest congestion that had persisted for months. Pulmonology workup revealed no mechanical or inflammatory issue in the lungs, yet he was prescribed an inhaler, which proved ineffective. His primary care provider suspected acid reflux and initiated famotidine, which also yielded no improvement.

What emerged during our initial consultation was the deep relationship between his symptoms and emotional stress. He described the sensation as "feeling like I have multiple sternums," a layered tension that tightened around the chest in response to stress, especially in mundane but activating situations, like getting stuck in traffic. His breathing wasn't labored in the classic respiratory sense; it was constricted by emotion, tension, and residual phlegm. The symptom pattern was inconsistent with straightforward pulmonary or gastric pathology but strongly suggested Liver Qi constraint in the chest, compounded by residual Phlegm, and possibly Blood Stasis, following his Covid infection.

We began with acupuncture, focusing on moving Liver Qi and opening the chest. He responded extremely well, noting a steady increase in symptom-free days with each successive treatment. This pattern of incremental improvement confirmed the Qi-based nature of his obstruction, as well as the presence of lingering phlegm binding the diaphragm and thorax.

To address the internal terrain, I prescribed Xue Fu Zhu Yu Tang, modified to suit his constitution. This classic formula, well-known for its capacity to treat Blood Stasis, resolve Qi constraint, and clear lingering pathogens, provided a foundational shift. As he began to feel more consistently clear-headed, less reactive, and reported improved breathing even in previously triggering scenarios, the diagnosis was confirmed.

Notably, the patient independently decided to move out of the city to help manage stress and improve quality of life. In support of this transition, I provided a large batch of modified Xue Fu Zhu Yu Tang and encouraged him to continue acupuncture as needed for stress modulation and to help maintain Qi circulation in a new environment. I also encouraged him to give fibrinolytic enzymes a try, first Nattokinase and then Lumbrokinase, if he noticed no improvement.

This case is a striking example of how Long Covid symptoms can masquerade as structural illness, even when the root lies in post-viral constraint and constitutional patterning. In this case, the lingering pathogen resided in the chest and diaphragm, not the lungs per se. And it was not merely the infection that injured him, but the post-viral reactivity of a system already strained by chronic stress and dysregulated emotion.

Where pharmacology failed, classical harmonizing strategies and channel-based treatment succeeded, not only in symptom relief, but in giving the patient a greater sense of agency over his trajectory. His case is a testament to the subtlety of Lingering Pathogenic Illness and the necessity of treating the person, not just the symptom.

Case 5

A 37-year-old patient with a longstanding diagnosis of Myalgic Encephalomyelitis (ME) and more recent Long Covid presented with a complex and debilitating symptom picture. Their ME diagnosis had been made prior to the pandemic, primarily due to fatigue and post-exertional dizziness. After contracting SARS-CoV-2, their condition worsened considerably, evolving to include severe post-exertional malaise, orthostatic intolerance, a seizure disorder, borderline heart failure, migraines, nausea, and anhedonia, the inability to experience pleasure, particularly in relation to food and daily life.

To manage some of these more acute and disruptive symptoms, especially the seizures and migraines, they had been prescribed midodrine, topiramate, aripiprazole, and modafinil. These offered some stabilization, but they failed to substantially improve their baseline function. As an herbalist themselves, the patient had also been self-administering high-dose berberine and potent mast cell stabilizers such as Forsythiae Fructus in an effort to manage immune flares and systemic inflammation.

However, from an immunological standpoint, both berberine and mast cell stabilizers have known drawbacks. Berberine can induce apoptosis in antigen-presenting cells (APCs), and mast cell stabilizers tend to dampen APC activity, potentially impairing immune clearance of persistent antigens. This therapeutic approach, while intelligent and well-informed, appeared to be suppressing inflammation at the cost of leaving deeper immune dysfunction unresolved.

I recommended the patient trial APC-Restore, my formula designed to stimulate APC function and restore immune recognition of lingering pathogens and debris. After two weeks, they experienced immunopathology in the form of vomiting, which we interpreted as a rapid immune mobilization, a "clearing reaction" that can occur when a long-dormant pathogen or metabolite is finally processed.

Following that response, the patient reported that their nausea was gone, their appetite and sense of enjoyment had returned, and their orthostatic intolerance and dizziness had diminished markedly. Their baseline energy threshold improved, and they were able to tolerate more physical and mental exertion without crashing.

I advised a pulsed administration strategy, periods on and off APC-Restore to prevent overstimulation while allowing the immune system time to recalibrate. The patient continues to experience gradual, meaningful improvements, using this targeted immune approach to complement their other symptom-management strategies.

This case underscores a central theme of Lingering Pathogenic Illness: immunosuppression can mask progress when what's needed is judicious immune activation. Even highly informed patients can miss this when symptom management takes priority over root cause resolution. But when APC exhaustion is addressed directly, the immune system regains its memory and its momentum.

Case 6

A 40-year-old woman with ME presented with a familiar but difficult dilemma: she could exercise once a week, but doing so would leave her completely depleted, requiring the entire following week to recover. This post-exertional crash pattern was central to her condition. Though she initially claimed she'd "always been this way," further reflection revealed that her symptoms began shortly after Hurricane Katrina, a moment she hesitated to name because of how often medical professionals reduce her complex illness to trauma or anxiety (as though those are not also bodily experiences).

Since that time, she had experienced fragmented sleep, persistent exertion intolerance, frequent illness, and, more recently, a year-long sensation of chronic urinary discomfort. Though multiple doctors had ruled out an active infection, she described the feeling as though she had a UTI that never fully resolved, a vague lower abdominal pressure, and urinary frequency with no clear microbial culprit.

To my clinical eye, this constellation of symptoms, chronic fatigue, sleep disruption, treatment-resistant urinary symptoms, and post-exertional malaise, suggested Kidney Qi deficiency with Dampness, possibly a Shaoyin level pathogen. The sleep disturbance, coming directly after Katrina, pointed toward a shock-related disintegration of Heart-Kidney communication, a common feature of Lingering Pathogenic Illness precipitated by trauma and exhaustion in the Shaoyin level.

I reassured her that Katrina was not an incidental life stressor, but a causative insult, a total-body trauma that created the conditions for deep immune and nervous system dysregulation. Many patients experienced illness onset or worsening following that disaster.

My initial prescription included Tian Wang Bu Xin Dan and Shen Qi Wan to rebuild Shaoyin integrity and support deep sleep and constitutional strength. I also recommended 500 mg of Reishi (Ling Zhi) for immune modulation and nervous system repair. She was unable to take nighttime formulas due to prescribed sleep medications, but began using Shen Qi Wan and Reishi during the day, and gradually began to report modest but noticeable improvements in baseline energy and constitutional tone.

She had never heard of ME or post-exertional malaise, so I very gently advised her not to push herself and sent along more information for reading. I also advised broader microbial screening of her urine in case of missed or atypical infection, while affirming that her lived experience made clinical sense even if it had long been dismissed. This case highlights how trauma-induced LPI often initiates in the Shaoyin axis, and how the body's undoing post-disaster may only begin to be reversed with equally sustained, validating, and thoughtful care.

Conclusion

It is my sincere hope that this handbook serves as a resource not just for clinicians navigating complex cases but for patients seeking understanding, empowerment, and tangible hope. Chronic illness can be isolating; understanding your journey through the lens of Lingering Pathogenic Illness can offer clarity, connection, and a renewed sense of possibility.

As we conclude, I want to emphasize that this is just one step on an evolving journey. Our understanding of immune health, chronic pathogens, and holistic treatment strategies continues to grow. Keep questioning, keep learning, and most importantly, keep believing in your capacity for healing. I look forward to learning more with you!

Glossary of Terminology

Anaerobic Glycolysis: A metabolic pathway that allows cells to generate energy (ATP) by breaking down glucose in the absence of oxygen. Instead of proceeding through the full mitochondrial oxidative cycle, glucose is converted to lactate, yielding rapid but inefficient energy production. While essential during acute stress or hypoxia, chronic reliance on anaerobic glycolysis reflects metabolic dysfunction, as seen in immune exhaustion, cancer, and persistent viral syndromes. It promotes acidosis, inflammation, and cellular fatigue. In TCM, this state resembles Qi Stagnation with Damp or Phlegm, where the system is forced to rely on short-term, inefficient energy, ultimately leading to depletion of Zheng Qi and accumulation of turbid byproducts.

Antigen-presenting Cell (APC): A type of immune cell, such as a dendritic cell, macrophage, or B cell, that processes and presents antigens to T cells, initiating and regulating immune responses. In chronic illness, APC dysfunction can impair both immune activation and tolerance, contributing to persistent inflammation and autoimmunity.

Autophagy: A cellular housekeeping process in which cells degrade and recycle their own damaged components, including misfolded proteins, dysfunctional organelles, and intracellular pathogens. Autophagy supports cellular health, regulates immune responses, and plays a critical role in maintaining metabolic balance. Dysregulation of autophagy is implicated in chronic infections, immune exhaustion, and neuroinflammatory conditions.

Barrier Dysfunction (Intestinal/Lung/BBB): Refers to the breakdown of protective epithelial or endothelial linings, such as the gut lining (intestinal barrier), lung alveolar membrane, or blood-brain barrier (BBB). When these barriers lose integrity, it allows translocation of pathogens, toxins, or immune complexes into tissues or circulation, triggering systemic inflammation. Barrier dysfunction is common in chronic illness and closely tied to immune dysregulation, microbial imbalance, and loss of tolerance.

Blood Level (Four Levels): The deepest level, where heat has penetrated the Blood layer, causing reckless movement of Blood or extreme internal heat. Signs include high fever, bleeding (e.g., nosebleeds, blood in stool), rashes, delirium, convulsions, and a deep red or crimson tongue. This stage often involves Yin collapse and severe Shen disturbance, requiring urgent intervention.

Blood Stasis (TCM): A pathological condition where Blood fails to flow smoothly, resulting in stagnation. It may manifest as fixed, sharp pain, dark or purplish complexion or tongue, or palpable masses. In chronic illness, Blood Stasis often reflects inflammation, circulatory impairment, or unresolved tissue damage. It is also metaphorically linked to emotional trauma and immune rigidity.

Candida: A genus of yeast-like fungi that commonly inhabit the human microbiome, particularly in the gastrointestinal and genitourinary tracts. While typically commensal, Candida can become opportunistically pathogenic when mucosal immunity is impaired or microbial balance is disrupted. In the context of Long Covid and ME/CFS, Candida overgrowth may emerge due to immune dysregulation, reduced secretory IgA, antibiotic use, or gut barrier dysfunction, contributing to symptoms such as bloating, brain fog, food intolerances, and fatigue. Chronic Candida may amplify innate immune activation and Th17-skewed responses, potentially reinforcing inflammatory loops already present in post-viral syndromes. Though not a root cause, Candida is considered a secondary burden that can exacerbate symptom persistence and metabolic stress in vulnerable patients.

Cheng Wu Ji: A prominent physician and commentator of the Song dynasty (12th century), Chéng Wǔ Jí is best known for his authoritative annotations on Zhang Zhongjing's *Shāng Hán Lùn* and *Jīn Guì Yào Lüè*. His edition of the *Shāng Hán Lùn* became the basis for the "Song edition," which remains the most widely transmitted version of the text. Chéng emphasized precise pattern differentiation and the correct matching of formulas to clearly defined clinical presentations, helping standardize and preserve classical doctrine during a period of textual instability. His work continues to shape the interpretation and clinical use of Zhang Zhongjing's teachings.

Chen Wuze (~1170 CE): A physician of the Song dynasty, best known for his work *Sanjin Fang* (*Formulas from the Three Categories*), which focused on classifying and treating externally contracted diseases. He contributed to the development of Warm Disease (Wen Bing) theory by distinguishing between different types of febrile disorders and emphasizing careful pattern differentiation. His work helped bridge classical Cold Damage theory with emerging approaches to epidemic and seasonal illnesses.

Collaterals: The branching vessels that extend from the primary channels to reach the body's surface, interior, and finer structures. Collaterals are the network of smaller channels that distribute Qi and Blood beyond the main meridians, ensuring communication between organs, tissues, and sensory or emotional pathways. They regulate circulation in areas not directly governed by the twelve regular meridians and play a key role in local symptoms, hidden pathogens, and chronic stagnation. Pathology in the collaterals often presents as tingling, numbness, fixed pain, or lingering heat. In warm disease theory and chronic illness, they are especially important when pathogens bypass the regular channels to embed deeper or more diffusely.

Cytomegalovirus (CMV): A beta-herpesvirus that establishes lifelong latency following primary infection, often asymptomatic in healthy individuals but capable of reactivation under immune stress. In the context of Long Covid and ME/CFS, CMV is significant for its ability to reshape the immune landscape, particularly through expansion of terminally differentiated T cells and chronic activation of innate immune pathways. Reactivation of CMV has been associated with inflammatory imprinting, immune exhaustion, and impaired antiviral responses, potentially contributing to persistent fatigue, cognitive dysfunction, and poor recovery in post-viral syndromes. Like EBV, CMV may act as a latent cofactor, aggravating immune dysregulation and interfering with the resolution of primary infections such as SARS-CoV-2.

Dampness (TCM): A heavy, turbid, and obstructive pathogenic factor that impairs Qi movement and fluid transformation. It can be external (from the environment) or internal (from Spleen dysfunction). Symptoms include fatigue, brain fog, loose stools, heaviness, and mucus. In biomedical terms, Dampness corresponds to metabolic waste accumulation, cytokine load, or lymphatic stagnation.

Da Yuan Yin: Translated as "Reach the Source Decoction," Da Yuan Yin was first recorded by Wu Youke in the *Wen Yi Lun* (Treatise on Epidemic Febrile Disease, 1642) as a treatment for epidemic pathogens trapped in the membrane source (膜原, *mo yuan*), the interstitial space between the diaphragm and the middle burner. The formula combines Hou Po, Cao Guo, Bing Lang, Zhi Mu, Huang Qin, Bai Shao, and Gan Cao to release constraint at this level, transform damp-turbidity, clear heat, and harmonize the Shaoyang. Classically, it was indicated for alternating fever and chills, chest and hypochondriac fullness, nausea, thirst with inability to drink, and a greasy yellow tongue coat. In modern practice, Da Yuan Yin and its variations are used to address Lingering Pathogenic Illness and post-viral syndromes, including Long Covid, where pathogens remain hidden in "in-between" spaces, producing cyclical symptoms such as digestive upset, neurological complaints, and alternating hot and cold sensations. Contemporary modifications, such as Qing Pi Tang, adapt the formula to strengthen Spleen Qi, clear residual heat, and calm the Shen. From a biomedical perspective, its actions may be understood as modulating immune dysregulation at barrier sites such as the gut-lung axis, where persistent pathogens and inflammatory mediators create cycles of inflammation and exhaustion.

Dendritic Cell (DC): A specialized type of APC that acts as a key messenger between innate and adaptive immunity. Dendritic cells capture antigens and migrate to lymphoid tissue to activate T cells. In chronic infections, dendritic cells may become exhausted or skewed toward an inflammatory phenotype.

Draining (xiè): Refers to the therapeutic reduction of excess, such as heat, dampness, or fire, through dispersal, elimination, or transformation. Unlike precipitation, which expels through the bowels, draining encompasses a broader range of techniques and organs, often using bitter, cooling herbs to clear pathogenic accumulation from the interior without necessarily inducing purgation.

Dysautonomia: A broad term describing dysfunction of the autonomic nervous system (ANS), which regulates involuntary functions like heart rate, blood pressure, digestion, and temperature. Symptoms may include dizziness, palpitations, GI disturbance, fatigue, and thermoregulatory issues. Common in Long Covid, ME/CFS, and other chronic inflammatory syndromes, dysautonomia is often secondary to immune or barrier dysfunction and can reflect deeper Qi and Yin depletion in Chinese medicine.

Dysregulation of Ying and Wei (TCM): In Chinese medicine, Ying Qi (Nutritive Qi) and Wei Qi (Defensive Qi) must harmonize to maintain health. Ying circulates in the interior, nourishing organs and tissues, while Wei circulates on the surface, protecting against external invasion. Dysregulation, often from chronic infection, overexertion, or latent pathogens, can result in immune confusion, manifesting as alternating fevers and chills, sleep disruption, or autoimmune-like patterns. In LPI, it reflects a loss of coordination between containment and expression of immune function.

Epstein-Barr Virus (EBV): A ubiquitous herpesvirus that establishes lifelong latency in B cells after initial infection, which is often asymptomatic or presents as mononucleosis. In the context of Long Covid and ME/CFS, EBV is clinically significant due to its potential for viral reactivation under conditions of immune stress or dysregulation. Reactivated EBV may contribute to chronic inflammation, fatigue, neurocognitive symptoms, and immune exhaustion, particularly through its effects on B cells, antigen-presenting cells, and cytokine signaling. Emerging evidence suggests that EBV reactivation may serve as a cofactor or amplifier in post-viral syndromes by compounding immune dysfunction and promoting viral persistence dynamics similar to those seen in Long Covid.

Essence (TCM): Known as "*Jing*," Essence is the deepest, most fundamental substance in the body, inherited at birth and gradually depleted through life. It governs growth, reproduction, and regeneration. In modern terms, it is often likened to constitutional vitality, neuroendocrine reserve, or mitochondrial resilience. An Essence deficiency can make one more vulnerable to Lingering Pathogenic Illnesses.

Extraordinary Vessels: Eight ancestral channels that regulate, integrate, and buffer the functions of the primary meridians. The Extraordinary Vessels act as reservoirs of Qi and Blood, governing inherited constitution, reproductive cycles, psycho-emotional integration, and the body's response to trauma or deep constitutional shifts. Unlike the twelve regular meridians, they do not correspond to Zang-Fu organs directly, but instead reflect prenatal influence (Jing), ancestral memory, and adaptive resilience. In clinical practice, they are often activated in complex, systemic, or treatment-resistant conditions, especially those involving hormonal regulation, chronic inflammation, or layered trauma.

FcγR (Fc Gamma Receptor): Receptors found on the surface of immune cells that bind to the Fc portion of IgG antibodies. There are activating and inhibitory types. Dysregulated FcγR signaling plays a major role in immune complex-mediated inflammation and is implicated in autoimmune and post-viral syndromes.

FcγRIIb (Fc Gamma Receptor IIb): The only known inhibitory Fc gamma receptor, expressed primarily on B cells and antigen-presenting cells. It helps downregulate immune activation by modulating antibody signaling. Impaired FcγRIIb function can lead to unrestrained inflammation and autoimmunity. Its dysfunction may be central to exaggerated immune responses in ME/CFS and Long Covid.

Floating Pulse (Fú Mài): A pulse that is most distinct with light pressure and weakens or disappears with deeper palpation. Traditionally associated with external invasions (e.g., Wind-Cold or Wind-Heat), it may also indicate deficiency at the surface, such as Wei Qi or Blood deficiency. In Lingering Pathogenic Illness, it can reflect unresolved pathogens near the exterior or a weakened ability to regulate surface defenses. Interpretation depends on context and accompanying pulse qualities.

FOXP3 Suppression: A state in which the expression or function of FOXP3, a master transcription factor for regulatory T cells (Tregs), is diminished. FOXP3 is essential for the development and immunosuppressive activity of Tregs, which maintain self-tolerance and restrain excessive immune responses. Suppression of FOXP3, whether through inflammatory metabolites like succinate, chronic cytokine signaling (e.g., IL-6, IL-1β), or mitochondrial dysfunction, results in loss of Treg stability, expansion of pro-inflammatory T cell subsets, and unchecked immune activation. In chronic illness, this contributes to immune dysregulation and tissue damage. In TCM, FOXP3 suppression mirrors a collapse of Liver/Kidney Yin or loss of internal governance (Heart-Kidney disharmony), allowing rebellious Yang (Wind, Heat) to flare unchecked.

Fú Xíe (Lingering Pathogen): A term used in Chinese medicine to describe a pathogenic factor that was not fully expelled during an acute illness. It may lodge in deeper levels of the body, causing chronic or fluctuating symptoms. Comparable to latent viruses, immune complexes, or unresolved inflammation in biomedicine.

Gallbladder (TCM/organ/channel): Associated with decision-making, courage, and the flow of bile in digestion. The Gallbladder channel is also key to Shaoyang dynamics and is often involved in conditions with alternation, constraint, or Dampness and Heat.

Ge Hong: A physician, alchemist, and scholar of the Eastern Jin dynasty (283–343 CE), best known for his text *Zhou Hou Bei Ji Fang* (*Handbook of Prescriptions for Emergencies*). Ge Hong advanced early infectious disease treatment, promoted the use of minerals and potent herbs, and contributed to Daoist internal alchemy. His work reflects a blend of pragmatic clinical medicine and spiritual cultivation, influencing later developments in Chinese pharmacology and longevity practices.

Gu Toxin (Gu Syndrome): A classical Chinese medicine concept describing complex, chronic, often parasitic or toxin-driven illness with psychological, digestive, and systemic symptoms. Originally associated with tropical disease and food poisoning, Gu now serves as a metaphor for difficult-to-treat, multi-system chronic illness involving lingering pathogens, dysbiosis, and immune disruption - such as in Long Covid and ME/CFS.

Hashimoto's Thyroiditis: An autoimmune disorder in which the immune system targets and gradually destroys the thyroid gland, most commonly leading to hypothyroidism. It is characterized by the presence of anti-thyroid peroxidase (TPO) and anti-thyroglobulin antibodies, along with lymphocytic infiltration of thyroid tissue. Hashimoto's involves impaired antigen-presenting cell (APC) regulation and loss of self-tolerance, often in the setting of Fc gamma receptor (FcγR) dysfunction and heightened type I interferon signaling. In the context of Long Covid and ME/CFS, Hashimoto's is notable both for its shared patterns of immune dysregulation and for its prevalence as a comorbidity. Fluctuating thyroid hormone levels may exacerbate fatigue, cognitive dysfunction, and thermoregulatory issues, making screening essential in patients with post-viral or chronic inflammatory syndromes.

Heart (TCM/organ/channel): Regulates blood circulation and houses the *Shen* (mind/spirit). Disorders may manifest as insomnia, palpitations, anxiety, or cognitive fog. Often affected by heat, Yin deficiency, or internal disruption of Blood.

HLA-DR (Human Leukocyte Antigen – DR Isotype): A major histocompatibility complex (MHC) class II molecule found on the surface of antigen-presenting cells. It presents extracellular antigens to CD4+ T cells, initiating adaptive immune responses. Reduced or absent HLA-DR expression on monocytes is a biomarker of immune paralysis or antigen-presenting cell dysfunction in sepsis, post-viral syndromes, and chronic inflammatory conditions.

Huang Di Nei Jing Su Wen / Ling Shu: The *Su Wen* ("Basic Questions") is one half of the foundational text *Huang Di Nei Jing* ("Yellow Emperor's Inner Classic"), compiled around the 2nd century BCE. Presented as a dialogue between the Yellow Emperor and his ministers, it outlines core principles of Chinese medicine, Yin-Yang, the Five Phases, Qi dynamics, seasonal adaptation, and the causes of disease, forming the theoretical basis for diagnosis and treatment. Often translated as the "Spiritual Pivot," the **Líng Shū** is the second half of the *Huang Di Nei Jing*. While the *Sù Wèn* focuses on theoretical principles, cosmology, and etiology, the Líng Shū centers on acupuncture, the channels and collaterals, and the dynamic movement of Qi. Rich in clinical detail and metaphysical insight, it provides the classical framework for understanding physiological communication and the regulation of life through the meridian system. The Líng Shū remains a core reference for the energetics of disease and intervention in traditional Chinese medicine.

Hypermobile Ehlers-Danlos Syndrome (hEDS): A connective tissue disorder marked by joint hypermobility, tissue fragility, and autonomic dysfunction. Often comorbid with MCAS and dysautonomia, hEDS is relevant to chronic illness because of its association with barrier dysfunction, immune dysregulation, and poor connective tissue repair. In TCM, it may correspond to congenital Kidney deficiency or Spleen failing to govern the flesh.

IDO Hyperactivation: The pathological overexpression of the enzyme indoleamine 2,3-dioxygenase (IDO), often triggered by chronic immune stimulation such as interferon-γ signaling. IDO breaks down tryptophan into kynurenine and other metabolites that suppress immune function. When overactive, IDO promotes immune tolerance, inhibits antigen-presenting cells, and contributes to T cell exhaustion and chronic inflammation. It is implicated in Long Covid, ME/CFS, cancer, and persistent viral syndromes.

IGg: A type of antibody involved in long-term immune defense and immune memory. IgG can form immune complexes that, when not cleared properly, lead to chronic inflammation and FcγR activation.

Immune Complex: A cluster of antigens bound to antibodies (usually IgG). If not cleared effectively by phagocytes, these complexes can deposit in tissues and perpetuate inflammation, a key feature of autoimmunity and Lingering Pathogenic Illness.

IRG-1 (Immune-Responsive Gene 1): A mitochondrial enzyme upregulated in innate immune cells during infection or inflammation. Its primary function is to catalyze the production of itaconate, a metabolite that modulates immunity by inhibiting succinate dehydrogenase (SDH) and dampening inflammatory signaling pathways. While itaconate helps resolve acute inflammation and prevent tissue damage, sustained IRG-1 activation can suppress mitochondrial function and impair antigen presentation. In chronic illness, this may contribute to immune tolerance, metabolic exhaustion, and APC dysfunction. In TCM terms, IRG-1 reflects the system's attempt to "cool Heat" and preserve Yin, but in excess, it may lead to Cold Phlegm, stagnation, and collapse of Zheng Qi.

Itaconate Shunt Theory: A modern immunometabolic theory describing how activated macrophages and dendritic cells divert the TCA cycle by converting cis-aconitate into itaconate via the enzyme IRG1. This shift reduces energy production while exerting antimicrobial effects (by inhibiting bacterial isocitrate lyase) and anti-inflammatory control (via SDH inhibition and Nrf2 activation). While protective in acute settings, sustained itaconate production may impair antigen-presenting cell (APC) function, contributing to immune exhaustion and chronic illness states such as Long Covid and ME/CFS. In Chinese medicine terms, this represents a Yin-like metabolic retreat, akin to latent heat, toxin retention, or Zheng Qi deficiency.

Jiang Baosu (1794–1873): Qing dynasty physician best known for his work *Yixue Yizhong Jiyan*. Jiang is notable for his careful clinical observations and emphasis on unresolved or atypical disease patterns - especially those that defied straightforward diagnostic categories. His case studies reflect a deep concern for illnesses that linger or transform over time, and his writings frequently reference the importance of treating what is hidden or obscured. Jiang's work serves as a bridge between classical theory and modern clinical complexity, preserving the legacy of lingering pathogenic illness as a legitimate and central concern of Chinese medicine.

Jin Gui Yao Lue: Translated as *Essential Prescriptions of the Golden Cabinet*, this classical text by Zhang Zhongjing focuses on the diagnosis and treatment of complex internal disorders. A companion to the *Shang Han Lun*, it emphasizes chronic illness, deficiency patterns, gynecology, and organ-based pathology, offering many foundational formulas still used in clinical practice today.

Jueyin: The deepest of the six stages in Chinese medicine, associated with the Liver and Pericardium channels. Imbalances may cause internal wind, heat rising, cold limbs, or contradictory symptoms. Often involved in persistent or relapsing conditions with circulatory or emotional disturbance.

Kidney (TCM/organ/channel): Stores Essence and governs growth, reproduction, and water metabolism. The Kidney is the foundation of Yin and Yang and supports the marrow, brain, and bones. Often implicated in chronic fatigue, endocrine disorders, and degenerative illness.

Large Intestine (TCM/organ/channel): Responsible for eliminating waste and maintaining bowel function. Paired with the Lung, it reflects the balance between intake and release. Frequently involved in Damp-Heat patterns, dysbiosis, and post-infectious bowel issues.

Lingering Pathogenic Illness: A condition in which remnants of an unresolved pathogen, such as viral debris or immune-metabolic signals, persist after acute illness or injury, leading to chronic symptoms like fatigue, brain fog, and immune dysregulation. This pattern underlies syndromes like Long Covid, ME/CFS, and chronic Lyme, and calls for phased treatment that alternates between expelling lingering pathogens and restoring Zheng Qi (Upright Qi).

Liver Detoxification: The liver's process of transforming and clearing toxins, hormones, and metabolic waste through Phase I (modification), Phase II (conjugation), and bile elimination. This system relies on nutrients like B vitamins and glutathione. Impaired detox can lead to toxin buildup, especially from sources like mold, which may contribute to inflammation, hormonal imbalance, and fatigue. In Chinese medicine, it parallels the Liver's role in coursing Qi and resolving internal constraint.

Liu Bao-Yi: A 19th-century physician and prominent advocate of the nourishing school in the late Qing dynasty. Known for emphasizing the importance of supporting Zheng Qi (upright or righteous Qi) rather than over-relying on harsh methods to expel pathogens, Liu famously argued that "in treating disease, one must first nourish the body's strength; only then can one expel the evil." His approach prioritized gentle, restorative treatment, especially in chronic or deficiency conditions, and stands as a counterpoint to more aggressive schools of thought in Chinese medicine.

Liver (TCM/organ/channel): Ensures the smooth flow of Qi and stores Blood. Imbalances may lead to stagnation, irritability, menstrual irregularity, or tendinomuscular tension. Also, central to detoxification and the emotional interface of chronic illness.

Liu Wansu: A prominent Jin dynasty physician (c. 1110–1200 CE) and founder of the "Cold and Cooling School" (Han Liang Pai). He emphasized the role of fire and heat in the pathology of many diseases and advocated the use of cooling herbs to clear heat and restrain Yang. Liu Wansu reinterpreted the *Huang Di Nei Jing* to support his view that many internal diseases arose from excessive heat, laying the foundation for later developments in Warm Disease (Wen Bing) theory.

Long Covid: A post-acute sequela of SARS-CoV-2 infection characterized by prolonged, multi-system symptoms including fatigue (often with post-exertional malaise), brain fog, dysautonomia, and chronic inflammation. It shares clinical features with ME/CFS, mast cell activation syndrome, and post-treatment Lyme disease. Emerging models suggest that immune complex persistence, antigen-presenting cell dysfunction, and loss of immune tolerance are key immunopathological drivers.

Long Ebola: A post-acute sequela of Ebola virus disease (EVD) characterized by persistent symptoms and delayed complications after apparent recovery. Its pathomechanism is thought to involve dendritic cell (DC) dysfunction during acute infection, which impairs antigen presentation and immune resolution. This allows the Ebola virus to persist in immune-privileged sites such as the eyes, central nervous system, and testes, where it may form latent or low-replication reservoirs. These reservoirs contribute to chronic inflammation, neurologic and ocular complications, and even viral recrudescence. Long Ebola offers a model for understanding other post-viral syndromes involving viral persistence and immune dysregulation, including Long Covid and ME/CFS.

Lung (TCM/organ/channel): Governs respiration, Wei Qi (defensive energy), and fluid metabolism. Frequently, the first system affected by external pathogens. In chronic illness, the Lung often suffers from residual heat, phlegm, or dryness.

Lyme Disease (Long Lyme, Chronic Lyme): An illness caused by infection with *Borrelia burgdorferi*, typically transmitted by ticks. While most acute cases resolve with antibiotics, a subset of patients experience long-term symptoms, termed Long Lyme or Chronic Lyme, including fatigue, cognitive changes, joint pain, and neurological dysfunction. Like Long Covid, it may involve persistent antigens, immune dysregulation, and disrupted homeostasis.

Macrophage: A phagocytic immune cell that engulfs pathogens, dead cells, and immune complexes. It also produces inflammatory cytokines and contributes to both tissue damage and repair. In LPI, macrophages may become hyperactivated or tolerized.

Mast Cell Activation Syndrome (MCAS): A condition in which mast cells release histamine and other mediators inappropriately, causing symptoms like flushing, rashes, digestive upset, brain fog, and anaphylaxis. MCAS often occurs alongside chronic infections, Long Covid, and connective tissue disorders. It reflects a state of immune hyper-reactivity and disrupted homeostasis, sometimes linked to loss of inhibitory FcγR signaling and barrier dysfunction.

MMP2/MMP9 Inhibition: Refers to the suppression of matrix metalloproteinases 2 and 9, enzymes that degrade extracellular matrix and contribute to tissue remodeling, inflammation, and vascular leakage. Herbal and pharmacologic inhibitors of MMP2/MMP9 (e.g., Dan Shen, Ling Zhi) are relevant in chronic illness for preventing immune-mediated tissue injury, fibrosis, and blood-brain barrier disruption, key pathologies in Long Covid, ME/CFS, and hEDS.

Mold: Various species of fungi that can grow indoors or in damp environments, producing spores and, in some cases, mycotoxins that affect human health. In the context of Long Covid and ME/CFS, mold exposure is significant as a non-infectious but immunologically active environmental trigger. For sensitive individuals, particularly those with impaired detoxification pathways, HLA-DR susceptibility, or prior immune compromise, mold exposure can provoke chronic inflammatory responses, mast cell activation, and neuroimmune dysregulation. Symptoms often mimic or compound post-viral syndromes, including fatigue, cognitive dysfunction, temperature instability, and post-exertional malaise. Mold is considered a perpetuating factor in recovery from viral illness, and unrecognized mold exposure may inhibit healing or lead to misattribution of symptoms to lingering infection alone.

Mo Yuan (Membrane Source): A classical Chinese medical concept describing an intermediate space between the interior and exterior. Pathogens lodged here are neither fully in nor fully out, leading to low-grade, chronic, or relapsing illness. Often involved in Shaoyang patterns and post-viral syndromes.

Myalgic Encephalomyelitis (ME/CFS): A chronic, multi-system illness characterized by post-exertional malaise, unrefreshing sleep, cognitive dysfunction, and profound fatigue. It often follows viral infection and involves mitochondrial dysfunction, immune dysregulation, and impaired energy metabolism. Closely associated with Long Covid in both pathophysiology and clinical presentation.

Orthostatic Hypotension (OH): A form of dysautonomia where blood pressure drops significantly upon standing, often leading to dizziness, lightheadedness, or syncope. Common in chronic fatigue syndromes, OH reflects impaired vascular tone and autonomic regulation. In TCM, it may reflect Qi, Yang, or Blood deficiency.

Paul Unschuld: A contemporary scholar and historian of Chinese medicine, best known for his translations and analyses of classical medical texts, including the *Huang Di Nei Jing* and *Nan Jing*. His work emphasizes the historical, philosophical, and political contexts of Chinese medical thought, often highlighting its differences from Western biomedical models. Unschuld's research has been influential in bringing critical academic attention to the conceptual foundations of Chinese medicine in the modern era.

Pericardium: The Heart's protector in Chinese medicine, responsible for shielding the Heart from heat pathogens and regulating emotional and Shen (spirit) activity. It plays a key role in febrile and emotional disorders, especially when heat reaches the Ying level and disturbs consciousness.

Phagocytosis: The process by which immune cells such as macrophages or dendritic cells engulf and digest cellular debris, pathogens, or immune complexes. Failure of this mechanism can lead to inflammation, autoimmunity, or persistent infection.

Phlegm (TCM): A congealed form of Dampness that obstructs the body more deeply, particularly the channels or sensory orifices. It may be visible (e.g., sputum, nodules) or invisible (e.g., brain fog, mental confusion, systemic inflammation). In chronic illness, Phlegm is often seen in neuroinflammatory states, lipid dysregulation, and immune overactivation.

Post-Chemotherapy Syndromes: A cluster of persistent physical, cognitive, and psychological symptoms that occur after the completion of cancer treatment, often lasting months or years beyond remission. These may include fatigue, brain fog, neuropathy, immune suppression, dysautonomia, and mood disturbances. Mechanistically, post-chemotherapy syndromes are thought to result from mitochondrial damage, chronic inflammation, and lasting alterations to immune surveillance, including dysfunction of dendritic cells and antigen-presenting pathways. Chemotherapeutic agents may also disrupt the gut microbiome and blood–brain barrier, compounding neuroimmune injury. In the context of Long Covid and ME/CFS, these syndromes are increasingly recognized as parallel expressions of acquired chronic illness, marked by overlapping features such as post-exertional malaise, autonomic dysfunction, and impaired recovery from stressors.

Post-Exertional Malaise (PEM): A hallmark symptom of ME/CFS and Long Covid characterized by a delayed worsening of symptoms (e.g., fatigue, pain, brain fog) following physical or mental exertion. PEM reflects metabolic inflexibility, mitochondrial dysfunction, and immune exhaustion. In Chinese medicine, it correlates with Qi and Yin deficiency compounded by latent pathogenic activity.

Post-Exertional Symptom Exacerbation (PESE): A broader term than post-exertional malaise (PEM), PESE refers to the worsening of a range of symptoms, not only fatigue, following physical, cognitive, or emotional exertion. These may include pain, orthostatic intolerance, immune flares, or neurocognitive dysfunction. PESE highlights the multisystem dysregulation underlying Long Covid and ME/CFS, including immune activation, impaired metabolic recovery, and autonomic instability. In Chinese medicine, PESE is understood as the destabilization of latent pathogens and dysregulation of Wei and Ying Qi coordination in response to strain on a deficient system.

Post-Exposure Malaise (e.g., Mold): An acute or delayed worsening of symptoms following exposure to environmental triggers like mold, chemicals, or allergens. Often seen in patients with mast cell activation, dysautonomia, or persistent immune activation. In TCM, it suggests lingering pathogen reactivation combined with Wind-Damp invasion and Wei Qi instability.

Postural Orthostatic Tachycardia Syndrome (POTS): A form of dysautonomia marked by an excessive heart rate increase upon standing (typically >30 bpm in adults, >40 bpm in adolescents), often accompanied by lightheadedness, palpitations, and fatigue. POTS is frequently seen in Long Covid and ME/CFS and is associated with hypovolemia, immune activation, mast cell dysfunction, and neurovascular dysregulation.

Precipitation (xià): A specific form of draining that forcefully expels accumulation or pathogens through the bowels. Distinguished by its strong downward action, it targets interior excess, such as heat, food, or blood stasis, and is used selectively when blockage is pronounced.

Pre-natal Qi: The foundational life force inherited at conception, derived from the essence of the parents. Pre-natal Qi is stored in the Kidneys and forms the basis of one's constitutional strength, vitality, and longevity. It governs growth, development, and the capacity for regeneration. Unlike Post-natal Qi, which is replenished through food, breath, and experience, Pre-natal Qi is finite and non-renewable, though it can be conserved and supported through careful lifestyle and treatment strategies. In modern terms, it parallels aspects of genetic inheritance, mitochondrial vigor, and baseline immune resilience.

Pulse Diagnosis (TCM): A key method for assessing internal health by palpating the radial artery at three positions on each wrist. Pulse qualities, such as depth, rate, strength, shape, and rhythm, provide insights into organ function, Qi, Blood, and fluid status. For instance, a deep, weak pulse may reflect Yang deficiency, while a wiry pulse may signal Liver constraint or pain. Pulse diagnosis helps confirm pattern differentiation and treatment direction.

Qi: The vital energy that powers all physiological processes in the body. It can be categorized as Wei Qi (defensive), Ying Qi (nutritive), or Yuan Qi (source/original). In chronic illness, Qi may become deficient, stagnant, or blocked. Qi is mostly intangible and used as a descriptor of measurement to define how well various systems are functioning in the body. According to the *Huang Di Nei Jing Ling Shu*, Qi is what warms the skin, fills out the body, and moistens the hair.

Qi Deficiency: A core diagnostic pattern involving fatigue, shortness of breath, poor digestion, and weak immunity. Qi is the animating force of all physiological functions. Deficiency may result from overwork, illness, or chronic inflammation. Common in LPI, where immune and metabolic systems become underpowered and recovery is impaired.

Qi Level (Four Levels): The stage where the pathogen has moved deeper into the interior, often manifesting as high fever, profuse sweating, thirst, irritability, cough with yellow sputum, and a full, rapid pulse. This level corresponds to excess heat in the Yang organs, especially the Lungs, Stomach, and Intestines.

Qi Stagnation: A blockage or improper circulation of Qi, often presenting as mood swings, tension, pain, or irregular menses. Stress, repressed emotion, or unresolved pathogens can impair Qi flow. In chronic illness, Qi stagnation may overlap with dysautonomia, trauma, mast cell activation, and impaired detoxification.

Qian Jin Yao Fang: Translated as *Essential Prescriptions Worth a Thousand Gold Pieces*, a monumental Tang dynasty medical compendium written by Sun Simiao, often revered as the "King of Medicine." Completed around 652 CE, this work contains more than 5,300 prescriptions, organized into 30 volumes, covering internal medicine, gynecology, pediatrics, surgery, acupuncture, moxibustion, and dietetics.

The title reflects Sun's conviction that life and health are worth more than a thousand pieces of gold. The text emphasizes preventive medicine, proper conduct of the physician, and the ethical duty to treat all patients equally, including women, children, and the poor, making it not only a clinical but also a moral landmark in Chinese medical history. Together with its companion volume, *Qian Jin Yi Fang* (Supplement to Prescriptions Worth a Thousand Gold Pieces), it laid a foundation for later medical practice and remains a key reference for classical formula study.

Redox Balance: The dynamic equilibrium between oxidation and reduction reactions that governs cellular energy flow, metabolic signaling, and oxidative stress. In physiological conditions, reactive oxygen and nitrogen species are balanced by antioxidant systems such as glutathione and superoxide dismutase, maintaining proper immune and mitochondrial function. When this balance is lost - through excess oxidant production or insufficient antioxidant capacity - oxidative stress arises, damaging cellular structures and impairing immune regulation. In chronic inflammatory or infectious states, persistent redox imbalance contributes to antigen-presenting cell exhaustion, mitochondrial dysfunction, and impaired recovery. In Chinese medicine terms, redox balance parallels the dynamic interplay of Fire (oxidative drive, metabolic activity) and Water (Yin containment, antioxidant capacity), reflecting the harmonious transformation of Qi and preservation of Yin.

San Jiao (TCM/organ/channel): The Triple Burner or Triple Heater, responsible for coordinating water and Qi movement across the body's three burners (upper, middle, lower). Often interpreted as a regulatory or metabolic network rather than a physical organ.

San Yin Ji Yi Bing Zheng Fang Lun: Translated as *Treatise on the Three Causes of Diseases*, Chen Wuze wrote this Song dynasty medical classic in 1174 CE. This text systematized the concept of the *three causes* (*san yin*) of disease: internal causes (neiyin), such as emotions; external causes (waiyin), such as wind, cold, damp, or heat; and non-internal-external causes (buyin feiyin), such as improper diet, overwork, or injury. Chen Wuze emphasized the role of constitutional weakness and pathological "root vs. branch" dynamics in the progression of illness. The work is also notable for its discussion of complex, mixed pathologies and the need for formulas that address multiple mechanisms simultaneously. *San Yin Ji Yi Bing Zheng Fang Lun* influenced later Ming and Qing physicians, including Ye Tianshi, and remains an important text for understanding the early synthesis of etiological theory in Chinese medicine.

Shang Han Lun: Translated as *Treatise on Cold Damage*, this seminal text by Zhang Zhongjing outlines the diagnosis and treatment of externally contracted febrile diseases. Based on the six-stage model (Taiyang to Jueyin), it provides a systematic approach to disease progression and contains many core formulas used to treat both acute and chronic conditions.

Shaoyang: One of the six divisions of channel theory, representing the pivot between interior and exterior. Dysregulation here leads to alternating symptoms (chills/fever, appetite swings), unresolved infection, and poor detoxification. Key in post-viral syndromes.

Shaoyin: The Yin-most of the six stages, involving the Heart and Kidney. Imbalances may lead to deficiency heat, Yang deficiency, or interior cold. Often implicated in fatigue, dysautonomia, and deep-level immune dysfunction.

Shen (TCM): Often translated as "spirit," Shen reflects consciousness, mental clarity, emotional balance, and the vitality of awareness. Rooted in the Heart, Shen can be disturbed by Heat, Phlegm, or Blood deficiency. In modern terms, it may relate to neuropsychiatric integrity, mood, and cognitive coherence.

Slippery Pulse (Huá Mài): A pulse that feels smooth, flowing, and rapid, like pearls rolling on a dish. It often indicates exuberance of fluids or physiological abundance and is classically associated with Dampness, Phlegm, stagnation, and heat. In acute illness, it may reflect an active pathogenic presence; in Lingering Pathogenic Illness, a slippery pulse can signal residual inflammatory debris, gut stagnation, or dysregulated metabolism contributing to immune burden. Its interpretation depends on context and pairing with other pulse qualities.

Small Intestine (TCM/organ/channel): Separates the clear from the turbid, both physically and mentally. Imbalances may involve digestive issues, fever, or urinary dysfunction. Paired with the Heart, it reflects clarity in both digestion and discernment.

Spleen (TCM/organ/channel): Transforms food into Qi and Blood, governs the muscles, and holds Blood in the vessels. Spleen Qi deficiency often underlies fatigue, poor digestion, edema, and chronic illness patterns involving Dampness.

Stomach (TCM/organ/channel): Controls receiving and ripening of food and fluids. Its harmony is essential for postnatal Qi production. Often involved in Damp-Heat, phlegm accumulation, and digestion-related manifestations of LPI.

Succinate Dehydrogenase (SDH): A key mitochondrial enzyme that functions at the intersection of the tricarboxylic acid (TCA) cycle and the electron transport chain (Complex II). SDH oxidizes succinate to fumarate, facilitating ATP production and maintaining metabolic flow. It also regulates intracellular succinate levels, which act as signaling molecules in inflammation. Inhibition of SDH, by metabolites like itaconate, leads to succinate accumulation, driving hypoxia-inducible factor (HIF-1α) stabilization, cytokine production (e.g. IL-1β), and inflammatory signaling. In chronic illness, impaired SDH activity contributes to immune dysfunction and metabolic stalling.

Sun Simiao: A renowned physician of the Sui and Tang dynasties (581-682 CE), often honored as the "King of Medicine." He is best known for his comprehensive texts *Qian Jin Yao Fang* (*Essential Prescriptions Worth a Thousand Gold*) and *Qian Jin Yi Fang* (*Supplement to the Thousand Gold Prescriptions*), which emphasize preventive care, ethical medical practice, and detailed clinical guidance. Sun integrated Daoist, Confucian, and Buddhist principles, elevating the moral and spiritual dimensions of medicine.

Systemic Lupus Erythematosus (SLE): A chronic, multisystem autoimmune disease characterized by the production of autoantibodies and immune complex deposition that leads to widespread inflammation and tissue damage. A central feature of SLE pathophysiology is Fc gamma receptor (FcγR) dysfunction, which contributes to defective clearance of immune complexes and aberrant activation of innate immune cells such as dendritic cells, macrophages, and neutrophils. Dysregulated FcγR signaling amplifies type I interferon responses and promotes a self-sustaining loop of autoimmunity, particularly affecting the skin, kidneys, joints, and central nervous system. In the context of Long Covid and ME/CFS, SLE serves as a model for chronic immune activation, antigen presentation abnormalities, and loss of tolerance, offering insight into post-viral autoimmunity and Fc receptor-mediated pathology.

Taiyang: The most external of the six stages, governing the Bladder and Small Intestine channels. Often, the first to respond to an external invasion. In lingering illness, unresolved Taiyang-stage disorders may sink deeper or recur.

Taiyin: Represents the Lung and Spleen channels. Taiyin imbalances are often marked by dampness, cold, fatigue, and immune deficiency, key features in post-viral and chronic inflammatory states.

Tao Hongjing: A polymath of the Southern Dynasties period (456-536 CE), Tao Hongjing was a physician, alchemist, and scholar who compiled and annotated the *Shen Nong Ben Cao Jing Ji Zhu* (*Collected Commentaries on the Classic of the Materia Medica*). He systematized herbal knowledge, distinguished between authentic and counterfeit substances, and integrated Daoist cosmology with medical theory, laying the foundation for later developments in Chinese pharmacology and internal cultivation.

Taxation Relapse (Láo Fù): A relapse of disease symptoms triggered by physical or mental overexertion during a phase of apparent recovery. Originally described by Zhang Zhongjing in the *Shāng Hán Lùn*, taxation relapse reflects a failure to conserve and replenish vital Qi following illness or mistreatment.

TCA Cycle: The tricarboxylic acid (TCA) cycle - also known as the Krebs or citric acid cycle - is a central metabolic pathway that takes place in the mitochondrial matrix, converting acetyl-CoA derived from carbohydrates, fats, and amino acids into ATP, NADH, and $FADH_2$ for cellular energy production. Beyond its role in bioenergetics, the TCA cycle provides intermediates for amino acid synthesis, redox balance, and immune cell metabolism. Disruptions in TCA flux are characteristic of chronic inflammation and immune exhaustion, where mitochondrial dysfunction limits ATP generation and shifts metabolism toward glycolysis or incomplete oxidation. In immune regulation, proper TCA cycling supports antigen presentation, cytokine signaling, and resolution of inflammation. In Chinese medicine terms, the TCA cycle mirrors the continuous transformation of Qi and Yang - governing metabolic warmth, movement, and vitality - while its failure reflects Qi deficiency and metabolic stagnation.

Toll-Like Receptor (TLR): A class of innate immune receptors that recognize molecular patterns from pathogens or damaged cells, initiating immune activation. TLRs trigger cytokine release and antigen-presenting cell maturation, serving as key gatekeepers between innate and adaptive immunity. In chronic illness, dysregulated TLR signaling may drive ongoing inflammation or immune tolerance. In Chinese medicine terms, TLRs reflect Wei Qi vigilance - too strong, they may generate internal Wind or Heat; too weak, they allow Lingering Pathogens to embed deeper into the system.

Tongue Diagnosis (TCM): A foundational diagnostic tool in Chinese medicine, in which the shape, color, coating, and moisture of the tongue reflect internal physiological and pathological states. The tongue body reveals Blood, Yin, and organ condition; the coating reflects the state of the Stomach, fluids, and external pathogens. For example, a red tongue with no coating suggests Yin deficiency, while a thick, greasy coat may indicate Damp-Heat or phlegm accumulation.

Toxoplasmosis: An infection caused by the protozoan parasite *Toxoplasma gondii*, which establishes chronic, often asymptomatic latency in host tissues, especially in the brain, eyes, and muscle. In immunocompetent individuals, the infection is typically controlled but not eradicated. In the context of Long Covid and ME/CFS, toxoplasmosis is significant for its potential to modulate neuroimmune signaling, impair microglial regulation, and alter dopamine and glutamate pathways. Latent *T. gondii* may reactivate or exert low-grade neuroinflammatory effects under conditions of immune dysregulation, possibly contributing to fatigue, mood disturbance, and cognitive dysfunction. While not considered a primary driver, it is viewed as a potential cofactor in post-viral illness, particularly in cases marked by persistent neuroinflammation or immune surveillance deficits.

Urinary Bladder (TCM/organ/channel): Stores and excretes urine; paired with the Kidney. Its channel passes through the back and connects with the brain. Often implicated in pain, tension, fluid imbalance, and post-viral dysautonomia.

Venting (tòu): is the method of opening surface or intermediary layers to release trapped or latent pathogens. It facilitates the outward movement of heat, toxins, or unresolved inflammation, often through the skin, sweat, or respiration, without forceful purgation. Venting is used when blockage is not fully interiorized and may accompany mild tonification or harmonization to prevent reburial.

Venous Insufficiency: A condition where blood flow from the legs back to the heart is impaired due to weakened or damaged vein valves. This leads to pooling of blood, swelling, heaviness, and often itching, especially around the ankles or lower legs. Chronic cases may cause skin discoloration, irritation, or ulceration. In Chinese medicine, it may relate to blood stasis and damp accumulation in the lower Jiao.

Wei Level (Four Levels): The defensive or most superficial layer of the body's response to warm pathogens. Symptoms include fever, slight chills, headache, sore throat, cough, thirst, and a floating, rapid pulse. This stage reflects early, external invasion, where Wei Qi (defensive Qi) is battling the pathogen on the surface.

Wei Qi: The body's defensive Qi, circulating on the surface and guarding against external pathogens. It governs immune vigilance, temperature regulation, and circadian rhythm. Weak Wei Qi can result in frequent infections, allergies, or hypersensitivities. Often compared to innate immunity.

Wen Bing Tiao Bian: Translated as *Detailed Analysis of Warm Diseases*, an influential Qing dynasty medical classic written by Wu Jutong and published in 1798 CE. The text systematized the theory of Warm Diseases (Wen Bing) - febrile epidemics caused by externally contracted "warm pathogens." Wu Jutong elaborated the *Four Levels* (Wei, Qi, Ying, Xue) as a framework for understanding the depth and progression of pathogenic heat, and he provided corresponding formulas for each stage, many of which remain standards in clinical practice (e.g., Yin Qiao San, Qing Ying Tang, Xi Jiao Di Huang Tang). The work marks a shift from the *Shang Han Lun*'s six-stage model of cold damage to a specialized theory of epidemic febrile disease, reflecting new clinical realities of the Qing period. *Wen Bing Tiao Bian* is considered the definitive text of the Warm Disease school, and its diagnostic structure continues to shape both modern Chinese medicine and integrative approaches to infectious disease.

Wen Bing Zong Lun: *Comprehensive Treatise on Warm Diseases*, this late Qing dynasty text by Zhou Xuehai (1856–1906) synthesized and critiqued centuries of *wen bing* (warm disease) theory. Drawing from earlier thinkers such as Wu Youke and Wu Jutong, Zhou offered a refined clinical framework for the diagnosis and treatment of febrile illnesses, latent heat, and lingering pathogenic conditions. He emphasized the importance of pulse-spirit discordance, membrane source pathology, and the danger of superficial resolution that conceals deeper, unresolved heat. The *Wen Bing Zong Lun* represents a mature evolution of epidemic disease theory in

Chinese medicine and remains an important reference for understanding chronic post-febrile syndromes.

Wen Yi Lun: A foundational medical text that introduced a groundbreaking theory of epidemic illness as caused by a unique category of external pathogens called li qi, pestilential or heteropathic qi, distinct from the six climatic excesses (wind, cold, damp, etc.) traditionally emphasized in Chinese medicine. Wu Youke argued that epidemic diseases arise from specific, transmissible influences that invade the body via the mouth and nose, contradicting dominant medical views of his time. His insights laid the intellectual groundwork for later developments in warm disease (wen bing) theory and are often cited as early formulations of a contagion model within TCM. Wen Yi Lun's core legacy is its recognition of how pathogens can linger internally after the acute phase has passed, a concept that continues to inform the modern treatment of post-viral syndromes, including Long Covid.

Wind (TCM): A primary external pathogenic factor characterized by sudden onset, movement, and variability. Wind is often the carrier for other pathogens (like Cold, Heat, or Damp) and is considered the "spearhead" of disease. It may manifest with symptoms such as tremors, spasms, vertigo, or migratory pain. Internally, Wind is associated with Liver dysfunction and may be linked to neurological or autoimmune activity in modern terms.

Wind-Cold Invasion: A classical Chinese medicine pattern describing the early stage of an external illness caused by pathogenic wind and cold entering the body's surface. Symptoms typically include chills, mild fever, headache, stiff neck, clear nasal discharge, and absence of sweating, with a floating and tight pulse. It reflects the Wei (defensive) Qi's struggle against external cold at the body's surface and is often treated by gently releasing the exterior and warming the channels.

Wu Jutong: A Qing dynasty physician (1758-1836 CE) known for systematizing Warm Disease (Wen Bing) theory through his influential text *Wen Bing Tiao Bian* (*Systematic Differentiation of Warm Diseases*). He introduced the concept of the

Membrane Source (Mo Yuan) as a key site where warm pathogens lodge, leading to lingering or relapsing illness. Wu emphasized early cooling and venting to prevent deep penetration of heat, and his work helped refine the diagnosis and treatment of epidemic febrile diseases and latent pathogens.

Wu Youke: A physician and medical theorist of the late Ming dynasty (1582–1652), Wu Youke is best known for authoring the *Wen Yi Lun* (*Treatise on Pestilence*), in which he proposed that epidemic diseases arise from a distinct class of pathogenic qi, li qi, that is transmissible, non-seasonal, and capable of invading through the mouth and nose. Challenging classical models that attributed illness solely to the six climatic influences, Wu laid the conceptual groundwork for understanding contagion and lingering pathogens in Chinese medicine. His work anticipated key elements of germ theory and deeply influenced the development of wen bing (warm disease) theory during the Qing dynasty.

Yang: The dynamic, warming, and active aspect of the Yin-Yang pair. Yang governs function, movement, transformation, and defense. Deficiency of Yang may present as cold limbs, fatigue, poor metabolism, or sluggish immunity. In biomedical analogues, Yang is often associated with mitochondrial output, hormonal activation, and thermoregulation.

Yang Lishan: A physician and commentator of the Qing dynasty (1705–?), Yang Lishan is known for his contributions to the interpretation and application of *wen bing* (warm disease) theory. He emphasized the importance of preserving source qi during and after febrile illness, warning against overuse of purgatives and excessive cooling therapies in weakened patients. Yang recognized that pathogens could linger in a concealed state, and advocated for a treatment strategy that balanced clearing heat with supporting the body's upright qi. His clinical sensibility brought nuance to the evolving epidemic disease discourse and helped shape a more restrained, qi-preserving approach to unresolved or post-acute illness.

Ye Tianshi: A leading physician of the Qing dynasty (1666-1745 CE) and a principal founder of Warm Disease (Wen Bing) theory. He developed the Four Levels model (Wei, Qi, Ying, Xue) to describe the progression of febrile illnesses caused by warm pathogens. Ye emphasized early, precise intervention to clear heat and protect Yin, and his work shifted focus from Cold Damage to epidemic febrile diseases. His clinical clarity and focus on pathogen depth continue to influence modern Chinese medicine.

Yilüe Yizhong Jiyan: Translated as *Collected Medical Insights from Doubts in Medicine*: A compilation of clinical reflections by Jiang Baosu (1794–1873). The text emphasizes case-based reasoning and unresolved pathologies, reflecting Jiang's deep engagement with lingering and atypical illnesses. It was originally compiled in the mid-19th century and remains a valuable source for Qing dynasty clinical thinking.

Yin: The nourishing, cooling, and restorative counterpart to Yang. Yin encompasses bodily fluids, Blood, Essence, and the structural and regenerative substrates of the body. Yin deficiency manifests as dryness, heat signs, restlessness, or insomnia. Biomedically, Yin is linked to parasympathetic tone, neuroendocrine reserves, and cellular repair capacity.

Yin Deficiency (Yin Damage): A pattern marked by depletion of the body's cooling and moistening functions, often after heat illness, overwork, or blood loss. Symptoms include night sweats, dry mouth, insomnia, and a red, peeled tongue. Also called "Yin damage," it can lead to empty heat and internal agitation, especially in later-stage or Shaoyin disorders.

Ying Level (Four Levels): The nutritive (Ying) Qi layer, reflecting deeper heat affecting the Heart and Pericardium. Symptoms include fever worse at night, restlessness, insomnia, dry mouth, and sometimes faint rashes or delirium. The tongue is deep red or crimson, and the pulse is thin and rapid. This level indicates that heat is beginning to injure Yin and disturb the Shen (spirit).

Ying Qi: Nutritive Qi that circulates within the vessels, nourishing the organs and tissues. It works with Blood to support cellular function and is closely tied to metabolic activity and repair. In chronic illness, weak or disrupted Ying Qi can lead to fatigue, pain, and tissue depletion.

Yuan Qi: Source Qi, derived from Essence (Jing) and stored in the Kidneys. It powers all physiological processes and underlies constitutional strength. Yuan Qi is distributed via the San Jiao and is foundational to both vitality and resilience. In modern language, it relates to mitochondrial reserve, neuroendocrine tone, and epigenetic inheritance. A deficiency of Yuan Qi may make one more prone to Lingering Pathogenic Illnesses.

Zhang Congzheng: A leading physician of the Jin dynasty (1156-1228 CE) and a key figure in the "Attacking School" of medicine. He believed that most illnesses were caused by external pathogens and emphasized purging, sweating, and vomiting to expel them. Zhang advocated aggressive treatment methods to restore balance and was known for his bold, pathogen-centered approach, which contrasted with more nourishing or harmonizing styles. His work helped shape discussions around the strength of Zheng Qi versus the force of pathogenic factors.

Zhang Zhongjing: A foundational physician of the Eastern Han dynasty (c. 150-219 CE) and originator of the Cold Damage (Shang Han) school. He authored the *Shang Han Lun* and *Jin Gui Yao Lue*, establishing the six-stage model of disease progression and many formulas still central to Chinese medicine. His work laid the foundation for treating externally contracted and internally generated illnesses through pattern differentiation.

Zheng Qi: Upright or righteous Qi, an umbrella term encompassing all protective and regulatory forces of the body, including Wei Qi, Ying Qi, and Yuan Qi. It is the body's capacity to resist and recover from illness. When Zheng Qi is weak, pathogenic factors may lodge or linger, leading to chronic illness.

Zhou Hou Bei Ji Fang: Translated as *Handbook of Prescriptions for Emergencies*, a classic medical text compiled by Ge Hong during the Eastern Jin dynasty(~340 CE). The title literally means "Formulas to Keep at One's Elbow for Emergencies," reflecting its practical intent as a ready reference for urgent care. The work preserves over 1,000 prescriptions covering infectious diseases, epidemics, poisoning, wounds, and other acute conditions, often using readily available herbs and materials. It is notable for early references to variolation (smallpox inoculation), as well as practical instructions for preventing and treating epidemic disorders long before germ theory. Ge Hong's emphasis on accessibility, adaptability, and speed of response influenced later public health approaches in Chinese medicine and established the text as one of the foundational handbooks of emergency and epidemic treatment.

Zhu Danxi: A major physician of the Yuan dynasty (1281-1358 CE) and founder of the "Yin-Supplementing School" (Zhi Yin Pai). He emphasized that most chronic illnesses stem from Yin deficiency and the overactivity of Yang, coining the phrase "Yang is always in excess; Yin is always insufficient." Zhu promoted nourishing Yin, clearing deficiency heat, and supporting the body's essence, influencing centuries of internal medicine and gynecology. His thought marked a shift toward treating internal depletion rather than external invasion.

References

Al-Hakeim, Hussein Kadhem, et al. "Tryptophan Catabolites, Inflammation, and Insulin Resistance as Determinants of Chronic Fatigue Syndrome and Affective Symptoms in Long Covid." *Frontiers*, 29 June 2025, www.frontiersin.org/journals/molecular-neuroscience/articles/10.3389/fnmol.2023.1194769/full.

Andrew L. Mellor, David H. Munn; "Tryptophan Catabolism and Regulation of Adaptive Immunity." *J Immunol* 15 June 2003; 170 (12): 5809–5813. https://doi.org/10.4049/jimmunol.170.12.5809

Baral R, et al. "Neem leaf glycoprotein matures myeloid derived dendritic cells and optimizes anti-tumor T cell functions." *Vaccine*. 2010;28(5):1241-1252. https://doi.org/10.1016/j.vaccine.2009.11.018

Bensky, Dan, et al. Chinese Herbal Medicine: Materia Medica. 3rd ed., Eastland Press, 2004

Cai-Xia Dong a b, et al. "Structural Characterization of Polysaccharides from Saposhnikovia Divaricata and Their Antagonistic Effects against the Immunosuppression by the Culture Supernatants of Melanoma Cells on Raw264.7 Macrophages." *International Journal of Biological Macromolecules*, Elsevier, 5 Mar. 2018, www.sciencedirect.com/science/article/abs/pii/S0141813018303271.

Chang, T., Yang, J., Deng, H., Chen, D., Yang, X., & Tang, Z.-H. (2022). "Depletion and dysfunction of dendritic cells: Understanding SARS-CoV-2 infection." *Frontiers in Immunology*, 13, 843342. https://doi.org/10.3389/fimmu.2022.843342

Text: *Sān Yīn Jí Yī Bìng Zhèng Fāng Lùn* (三因極一病證方論)

Section: On Hidden Pathogens (伏邪篇)

Attributed Author: Chen Wuze (陳無擇, died ca. 1170)

Original: "邪氣伏而不表，當察於血。"

Translation: "When evil Qi does not manifest on the surface, one must examine the blood."

Chen, Y., Yang, W., Chen, F., & Cui, L. (2022). "COVID-19 and cognitive impairment: neuroinvasive and blood–brain barrier dysfunction." *Journal of Neuroinflammation*, 19, Article 222.

Chun-Yi Chuang a b, et al. "Salvianolic Acid a Suppresses MMP-2 Expression and Restrains Cancer Cell Invasion through Erk Signaling in Human Nasopharyngeal Carcinoma." *Journal of Ethnopharmacology*, Elsevier, 22 Jan. 2020, www.sciencedirect.com/science/article/abs/pii/S0378874119341340.

Text: *Rùmén Shìqīn* (儒門事親)

Section: On Treating Latent Disease through Expulsion

Attributed Author: Zhang Congzheng (張從正, 1156–1228)

Original: "病雖已去，而濁氣未清，當攻之。"

Translation: "Even when the disease appears to have passed, if turbid Qi has not cleared, it must be expelled."

Cooper, E. (2009). "New Enzyme Complex Isolated From Earthworms Is Potent Fibrinolytic." *Clinical Education.* https://www.clinicaleducation.org/resources/reviews/potent-natural-fibrinolytic-enzymes-safely-reduce-clotting-risk/

Cooper, E. (2009). “Two Doctors Report on the Use of Lumbrokinase in Lyme Disease: This Enzyme Complex Helps Potentiate Antibiotics and Antimicrobials.” *Clinical Education*. https://www.clinicaleducation.org/wp-content/uploads/argfocus_200903_earthworms_web.pdf

Edwards, J., Cambridge, G., & Cliff, J. M. (2025). “A proposed mechanism for ME/CFS invoking macrophage FcγRI and interferon gamma.” Preprint, *Qeios*. https://doi.org/10.32388/8GI3CT

Text: *Zhòu Hòu Bèi Jí Fāng* (肘後備急方)

Attributed Author: Ge Hong (葛洪)Section: Cold Damage & Hidden Pathogens

Original: “邪留骨中不出。”

Translation: “The pathogen remains in the bones and does not come out.”

Gao, P., Li, X., Ding, J., Peng, B., Munir, M., Liu, F., Chao, L., Li, C., Wang, L., Ma, J., & Zhang, G. (2025). “Antiviral and Immune Enhancement Effect of Platycodon grandiflorus in Viral Diseases: A Potential Broad-Spectrum Antiviral Drug.” *Molecules*, 30(4), 831.

Georgopoulos AP, James LM, Peterson PK. “Human Leukocyte Antigen (HLA) at the Root of Persistent Antigens and Long COVID.” *J Immunol* Sci. 2025 Jan 6;9(1):1-3. doi: 10.29245/2578-3009/2025/1.1257. PMID: 39949480; PMCID: PMC11823424.

Guerrera, Giorgia, et al. “Identification of an Immunological Signature of Long COVID Syndrome.” *Frontiers in Immunology*, vol. 15, 2025, article 1502937, https://doi.org/10.3389/fimmu.2024.1502937

Han SB, et al. "A polysaccharide isolated from Pueraria lobata enhances maturation of murine dendritic cells." *Int J Biol Macromol*. 2013;52:184-191.

Text: *Huáng Dì Nèi Jīng Sù Wèn* (黃帝內經·素問)

Section: Chapter 58 — Qì Jiāo Biàn Dà Lùn (氣交變大論)

Original: "邪之所凑，其氣必虛。"

Translation: "Wherever pathogenic Qi gathers, the Qi must be deficient."

Text: *Huáng Dì Nèi Jīng Sù Wèn* (黃帝內經·素問),

Section: Chapter 3: Shēng Qì Tōng Tiān Lùn (生氣通天論).

Original: "邪氣之客於身也，深者留之，淺者出之。"

Translation: "When pathogenic Qi lodges in the body: if it is deep, it remains; if shallow, it is released."

Hu D, Gao J, Yang X, Liang Y. "A Comprehensive Mini-Review of Curcumae Radix: Ethnopharmacology, Phytochemistry, and Pharmacology." *Natural Product Communications*. 2021;16(5). doi:10.1177/1934578X211020628

Hu, J.-L., Nie, S.-P., Li, C., Fu, Z.-H., & Xie, M.-Y. (2014). "A novel polysaccharide from the seeds of Plantago asiatica L. induces dendritic cells maturation through toll-like receptor 4." *International Immunopharmacology*, 18(2), 236–243.

Jia, K., Meng-Ting, L., Shuyang, X., Jianpeng, M., Ming-Yuan, L., & Yan, H. (2023). "Advances for pharmacological activities of Polygonum cuspidatum – A review." *Pharmaceutical Biology*, 61(1), 177–188.

Jiaxin Zhou a b, et al. "Codonopsis Pilosula Polysaccharide Alleviates Ulcerative Colitis by Modulating Gut Microbiota and SCFA/GPR/NLRP3 Pathway." *Journal of Ethnopharmacology, Elsevier*, 10 Oct. 2024, https://doi.org/10.1016/j.jep.2024.118928

Jin JO, et al. "Rehmannia glutinosa polysaccharide promoted activation of human dendritic cells." *Int J Biol Macromol.* 2018;116:232-238.

Juedes, A. E., & von Herrath, M. G. (2003). "Using regulatory APCs to induce/maintain tolerance." *Annals of the New York Academy of Sciences*, 1005, 128–137. https://doi.org/10.1196/annals.1288.014

Kang, S., & Min, H. (2012). "Ginseng, the "Immunity Boost": The Effects of Panax ginseng on the Immune System." *Journal of Ginseng Research*, 36(4), 354–368. https://doi.org/10.5142/jgr.2012.36.4.354

Kim HS, Shin BR, Lee HK, Park YS, Liu Q, Kim SY, Lee MK, Hong JT, Kim Y, Han SB. "Dendritic cell activation by polysaccharide isolated from Angelica dahurica." *Food Chem Toxicol.* 2013 May;55:241-7. doi: 10.1016/j.fct.2012.12.007. Epub 2012 Dec 14. PMID: 23246459.

Klein, J., Wood, J., Jaycox, J.R. et al. "Distinguishing features of long COVID identified through immune profiling." *Nature* 623, 139–148 (2023). https://doi.org/10.1038/s41586-023-06651-y

Krishna, B. A., Lim, E. Y., Metaxaki, M., Jackson, S., Mactavous, L., Lyons, P. A., Doffinger, R., Bradley, J. R., Smith, K. G. C., Sinclair, J., Matheson, N. J., Lehner, P. J., Sithole, N., & Wills, M. R. (2024). "Spontaneous, persistent, T cell–dependent IFN-γ release in patients who progress to Long COVID." *Science Advances*, 10(7), eadi9379. https://doi.org/10.1126/sciadv.adi9379

Kumar S, et al. "Neem (Azadirachta indica): prehistory to contemporary medicinal uses to humankind." *Asian Pac J Trop Biomed.* 2016;6(7):505-514.

Lee CK, et al. "Acemannan purified from Aloe vera induces phenotypic and functional maturation of immature dendritic cells." *Int Immunopharmacol.* 2001;1(7):1275-1284. https://doi.org/10.1016/S1567-5769(01)00052-2

Lei H, Wang X, Zhang Y, Cheng T, Mi R, Xu X, Zu X, Zhang W. "Herba Cistanche (Rou Cong Rong): A Review of Its Phytochemistry and Pharmacology." *Chem Pharm Bull* (Tokyo). 2020;68(8):694-712. doi: 10.1248/cpb.c20-00057. PMID: 32741910.

Text: *Clinical Handbook of Internal Medicine, Volume 3: Qi Blood Fluid Channels*
Attributed Author: Lei Shou-Yi (雷守儀), as cited in Maclean, William; Lyttleton, Jane; Bayley, Mark; Taylor, Kathryn Edition: 3rd Volume, 1st Edition Publisher: Eastland Press, 2010
Quotation (as cited): "The outward expression of lingering pathogen must follow the weak spots in channel Qi; there is no fixed route out of the body."Note: This quote is attributed to Lei Shou-Yi in the context of lingering pathogens (伏邪) but may be a paraphrase or lineage transmission. The original source text is not explicitly cited.

Li, N., Zhang, J.-Y., Zeng, K.-W., Zhang, L., Che, Y.-Y., & Tu, P.-F. (2012). "Anti-inflammatory homoisoflavonoids from the tuberous roots of Ophiopogon japonicus." *Fitoterapia*, 83(6), 1042–1045.

Text: *Wēn Rè Fēng Yuán* (溫熱逢原)
Section: Discussion of Treatment Principles for Residual Pathogens (論治伏邪)

Attributed Author: Liu Bao-Yi (劉保儀, 1842–1901)

Original: "不可用辛熱之劑，發散太過；亦不可用寒涼之藥，阻其外達。"

Translation: "Although it's inappropriate to use pungent and warm dispersing methods, one should also avoid using cold herbs that hinder the pathogen's outward movement."

Text: *Wēn Rè Fēng Yuán* (溫熱逢原)

Section: Treatise on Residual Pathogens (論伏邪病)

Attributed Author: Liu Bao-Yi (劉保儀, 1842–1901)

Original: "伏邪之病，最為常見，《內經》《難經》《傷寒》皆有之，非奇說也。"

Translation: "Lingering pathogens are a very common illness. They are recorded in the Nei Jing, Nan Jing, and Shang Han Lun; this is not a strange theory."

Text: *Wēn Rè Fēng Yuán* (《溫熱逢原》)

Section: 論伏溫邪 ("On Lurking Warm Pathogens")

Attributed Author: Liu Bao-Yi (劉保儀, 1842–1901)

Original: "伏溫之邪，層層深入，層層解去，然後為愈。每層之邪，較前一層更甚。"

Translation: "Lurking warm pathogens have many layers. After resolution and a cessation, one may proceed to evict through the next layer. Moreover, the pathogen of subsequent layers will invariably be more fixed than the first."

Liu, R., Zhang, X., Cai, Y., Xu, S., Xu, Q., Ling, C., Li, X., Li, W., Liu, P., & Liu, W. (2024). "Research progress on medicinal components and pharmacological activities of Polygonatum sibiricum." *Journal of Ethnopharmacology*, 328, 118024.

Text: *Su Wen Xuan Ji Yuan Bing Shi* (素問宣明原病式)

Section: On Internal Fire and Latent Heat

Attributed Author: Liu Wansu (劉完素, 1110-1200)

Original: "火氣不除，內伏為病根。"

Translation: "When fire Qi is not extinguished, it hides within and becomes the root of disease."

Li, X., Gui, R., Wang, X., Ning, E., Zhang, L., Fan, Y., Chen, L., Yu, L., Zhu, J., Li, Z., Wei, L., Wang, W., Li, Z., Wei, Y., & Wang, X. (2023). "Oligosaccharides isolated from Rehmannia glutinosa protect LPS-induced intestinal inflammation and barrier injury in mice." *Frontiers in Nutrition*, 10, 1139006.

Heidi Lovie. "Gu Syndrome, Lurking Pathogens, and Long Covid: An Old Take on a New Disease." *Medical Acupuncture*, vol. 33, no. 6, 2021, pp. 341–343. PMC8594969.

Lyttleton, Jane, and William Maclean. *Clinical Handbook of Internal Medicine: The Treatment of Disease with Traditional Chinese Medicine, Vol. 3: Qi, Blood, Fluid and Channel Disorders*. Seattle: Eastland Press, 2019.

Naidu, A. S., Wang, C.-K., Rao, P., Mancini, F., Clemens, R. A., Wirakartakusumah, A., Chiu, H.-F., Yen, C.-H., Porretta, S., Mathai, I., & Naidu, S. A. G. (2024). "Precision nutrition to reset virus-induced human metabolic reprogramming and dysregulation (HMRD) in long-COVID." *NPJ Science of Food*, 8(1), Article 19.

Narges Bordbar a, et al. "The Effect of Glycyrrhizin on Maturation and T Cell Stimulating Activity of Dendritic Cells." *Cellular Immunology*, Academic Press, 1 Dec. 2012, www.sciencedirect.com/science/article/abs/pii/S0008874912002079.

Noviello, M., Manfredi, M., Bongiovanni, D., et al. (2024). "The longitudinal characterization of immune responses in COVID-19 patients reveals novel prognostic signatures for disease severity, patients' survival and Long COVID." *Frontiers in Immunology*, 15, 1381091. https://doi.org/10.3389/fimmu.2024.1381091

Park, S.-Y., Truong, V.-L., Jeon, S.-G., Choe, S.-Y., Rarison, R. H. G., Yoon, B.-H., Park, J.-W., Jeong, H.-J., & Jeong, W.-S. (2025). "Anti-inflammatory and prebiotic potential of ethanol extracts and mucilage polysaccharides from Korean yams (Dioscorea polystachya and Dioscorea bulbifera)." *Foods*, 14(2), 173.

Pasharawipas, T. (2025). "Perspective: Host factor variants and the underlying causes of Long COVID." *Frontiers in Medicine*, 12, 1603317. https://doi.org/10.3389/fmed.2025.1603317

Ren, Z., Wang, C., Wang, T., Ding, H., Zhou, M., Yang, N., Liu, Y., & Chan, P. (2019). "Ganoderma lucidum extract ameliorates MPTP-induced parkinsonism and protects dopaminergic neurons from oxidative stress via regulating mitochondrial function, autophagy, and apoptosis." *Acta Pharmacologica Sinica*, 40(4), 441–450.

Rizal, A., Sandra, F., Fadlan, M. R., & Sargowo, D. (2020). "Ganoderma lucidum Polysaccharide Peptide Reduce Inflammation and Oxidative Stress in Patient with Atrial Fibrillation." *The Indonesian Biomedical Journal*, 12(4), 384–389.

Sahagún, A. M., Vaquera, J., García, J. J., Calle, Á. P., Diez, M.-J., Fernández, N., Loro, J. F., Portilla, H. O., & Sierra, M. (2015). "Study of the protective effect on intestinal mucosa of the hydrosoluble fiber Plantago ovata husk." *BMC Complementary and Alternative Medicine*, 15, 298.

Seoane, Paula I., et al. "Viral Infection Triggers Interferon-Induced Expulsion of Live Cryptococcus Neoformans by Macrophages." *PLOS Pathogens, Public Library of Science*, journals.plos.org/plospathogens/article?id=10.1371%2Fjournal.ppat.1008240. Accessed 19 June 2025.

Shan F, et al. "Modulation of phenotypic and functional maturation of murine dendritic cells by purified Achyranthes bidentata polysaccharide." *Int Immunopharmacol.* 2011;11(8):1103-1108. https://doi.org/10.1016/j.intimp.2011.03.006

Shi W, et al. "Structural characterization and adjuvant activity of a water soluble polysaccharide from Poria cocos." *Int J Biol Macromol.* 2024;273:133067. https://doi.org/10.1016/j.ijbiomac.2024.133067

Singh, R., Hemati, H., Bajpai, M., Yadav, P., Maheshwari, A., Kumar, S., Agrawal, S., Sevak, J. K., Islam, M., Mars, J. S., Sarin, S. K., & Trehanpati, N. (2021). "Sustained expression of inflammatory monocytes and activated T cells in COVID-19 patients and recovered convalescent plasma donors." *Immunity, Inflammation and Disease*, 9(4), 1396–1407. https://doi.org/10.1002/iid3.476

Sun, Y., Zhang, Z., Qiao, Q. et al. "Immunometabolic changes and potential biomarkers in CFS peripheral immune cells revealed by single-cell RNA sequencing." *J Transl Med* 22, 925 (2024). https://doi.org/10.1186/s12967-024-05710-w

Text: *Qiān Jīn Yào Fāng* (千金要方)
Section: Volume 1 — On the Art of Medicine (大醫精誠篇) and later discussions of Chronic Illness

Attributed Author: Sun Simiao (孫思邈, 581–682 CE)

Original: "上工治未病。"

Translation: "The highest skill is to treat illness before it arises."

Tang, Jiawen, and Xueying Zhao. "Research Progress on Regulation of Immune Response by Tanshinones and Salvianolic Acids of Danshen (Salvia Miltiorrhiza Bunge)." *MDPI*, Multidisciplinary Digital Publishing Institute, 7 Mar. 2024, www.mdpi.com/1420-3049/29/6/1201.

Text: *Shén Nóng Běn Cǎo Jīng Jí Zhù* (神農本草經集注)

Section: Commentary on Toxic Substances and Gu (毒藥·蠱毒)

Attributed Author: Tao Hongjing (陶弘景, 456–536 CE)

Original: "蠱毒之變化無窮，久留則中人神氣。"

Translation: "The transformations of Gu toxin are endless; when retained long-term, it can strike both the body and the spirit."

Tao, X., Liu, H., Xia, J., Zeng, P., Wang, H., Xie, Y., Wang, C., Cheng, Y., Li, J., Zhang, X., Zhang, P., Chen, S., Yu, H., & Wu, H. (2022). "Processed product (Pinelliae Rhizoma Praeparatum) of Pinellia ternata (Thunb.) Breit. alleviates the allergic airway inflammation of cold phlegm via regulation of PKC/EGFR/MAPK/PI3K-AKT signaling pathway." *Journal of Ethnopharmacology*, 295, 115449.

Umeyama A, Yahisa Y, Okada M, Okayama E, Uda A, Shoji N, Lee JJ, Takei M, Hashimoto T. "Triterpene esters from Uncaria rhynchophylla drive potent IL-12-dependent Th1 polarization." *J Nat Med.* 2010 Oct;64(4):506-9. doi: 10.1007/s11418-010-0438-1. Epub 2010 Jun 29. PMID: 20585989.

Paul U. Unschuld, *Medicine in China: A History of Ideas* (Berkeley: University of California Press, 1985), 33–41.

Van Booven, D. J., Gamer, J., Joseph, A., Perez, M., Zarnowski, O., Pandya, M., Collado, F., Klimas, N., Oltra, E., & Nathanson, L. (2023). "Stress-induced transcriptomic changes in females with Myalgic Encephalomyelitis/Chronic Fatigue Syndrome reveal disrupted immune signatures." *International Journal of Molecular Sciences*, 24(3), 2698. https://doi.org/10.3390/ijms24032698

Wang, Y., Lu, C., Huang, H., Yao, S., Xu, C., Ye, Y., Gui, S., & Li, G. (2020). "A lipid-soluble extract of Pinellia pedatisecta Schott orchestrates intratumoral dendritic cell-driven immune activation through SOCS1 signaling in cervical cancer." *Journal of Ethnopharmacology*, 267, 112837.

Text: *Wēn Yì Lùn* (瘟疫論)

Section: Preface and General Discussion of Pestilential Qi (瘟疫總論)

Wong, C. K., Leung, K. N., Fung, K. P., & Choy, Y. M. (1994). "The immunostimulating activities of anti-tumor polysaccharides from Pseudostellaria heterophylla." *Immunopharmacology*, 28(1), 47–54.

Text: *Wēn Bìng Tiáo Biàn* (溫病條辨)

Section: General Introduction and Commentary on Four-Level Differentiation (四層辨證總論)

Attributed Author: Wu Jutong (吳鞠通, 1758–1836)

Original: "衛氣營血辨證，條分縷析，以明病之淺深。"

Translation: "The differentiation of Wei, Qi, Ying, and Blood allows for precise analysis of the depth and progression of disease."

Text: *Wēn Bìng Tiáo Biàn* (溫病條辨)

Section: Differentiation of Ying-Level Disorders (辨營分證)

Attributed Author: Wu Jutong (吳鞠通, 1758–1836)

Original: "營分證，其證夜熱早涼，舌絳而乾，神煩少寐，或時譫語。"

Translation: "Ying-level disorders present with fever worse at night, crimson dry tongue, agitation with little sleep, or occasional delirious speech."

Wu, M. C. L., Italiano, E., Jarvis-Child, R., Alwis, I., Smythe, R., Albornoz, E. A., Noonan, J., Portelli, M., Baptista, M., Maclean, J., Noori, P., Yang, J., Lee, J. D., McFadyen, J. D., Sharland, A. F., Woodruff, T. M., Samson, A. L., Rapkiewicz, A., Barrett, T. J., Pham, A., Schoenwaelder, S. M., Yuan, Y., & Jackson, S. P. (2025). "Ischaemic endothelial necroptosis induces haemolysis and COVID-19 angiopathy." *Nature*, 618(7967), 123–130.

Wu, X.-D., Wang, C., Zhang, Z.-Y., Fu, Y., Liu, F.-Y., & Liu, X.-H. (2014). "Puerarin attenuates cerebral damage by improving cerebral microcirculation in spontaneously hypertensive rats." *Evidence-Based Complementary and Alternative Medicine*, 2014, Article ID 408501.

Attributed Author: Wu Youke (吳又可, 1582–1652)

Original: "毒氣伏於內，久而不發，遇虛則發。"

Translation: "Toxic Qi may hide internally and not erupt for a long time; when weakness arises, it emerges."

Yamada, D. H., Elsaesser, H., Lux, A., Timmerman, J. M., Morrison, S. L., de la Torre, J. C., Nimmerjahn, F., & Brooks, D. G. (2015). "Suppression of Fcγ-Receptor-Mediated Antibody Effector Function during Persistent Viral Infection." *Immunity*, 42(2), 379–390.

Yan De-xin. *Aging and Blood Stasis: A New TCM Approach to Geriatrics*. Translated by Philip Sinnott. Paradigm Publications, 2004

Yavropoulou, M. P., Tsokos, G. C., Chrousos, G. P., & Sfikakis, P. P. (2022). "Protracted stress-induced hypocortisolemia may account for the clinical and immune manifestations of Long COVID." *Clinical Immunology*, 245, 109133.

Text: *Wēn Rè Lùn* (溫熱論)Section: Ying and Blood Level Patterns (營分、血分篇)Attributed Author: Ye Tianshi (葉天士, 1666–1745)

Original: "伏熱不作熱，而作煩與燥。"

Translation: "When Heat hides, it does not manifest as fever, but as restlessness and dryness."

Text: *Wēn Rè Lùn* (溫熱論)

Section: Discussion of Warm Heat Entering the Membrane Source (溫熱犯膜原)

Attributed Author: Ye Tianshi (葉天士, 1666–1745)

Original: "邪伏膜原，不即傳經。"

Translation: "The pathogen is trapped in the Membrane Source and does not immediately transmit to the channels."

Text: *Wēn Bìng Lùn* (溫病論)

Section: Initial Discussion of Spring Warmth (春溫初起)

Attributed Author: Ye Tianshi (葉天士, 1666–1745)

Original: "身熱不惡寒者，熱伏於裏也。"

Translation: "When the body is hot without aversion to cold, the Heat is lodged in the interior."

Text: *Wēn Rè Lùn* (溫熱論), Discussion of Post-Heat Injury

Attributed Authors:Ye Tianshi (葉天士, 1666–1745)

Original (Ye Tianshi): "熱退之後，汗自出，神疲乏力。"Translation: "After the heat recedes, spontaneous sweating and fatigue of the spirit appear."

Text: *Wēn Rè Lùn* (溫熱論)

Attributed Author: Ye Tianshi (葉天士, 1666–1745)

Commentary (Ye Tianshi): "膜原者，非臟腑之內，非經絡之外。"Translation: "The membrane source is neither within the organs nor outside the channels."

Yong-Sheng Cui, Yi-Xuan Li, Si-Liang Jiang, An-Ning Song, Zheng Fu, Cai-Xia Dong, Zhi Yao, Wei Qiao, "Isolation, purification, and structural characterization of polysaccharides from Atractylodis Macrocephalae Rhizoma and their immunostimulatory activity in RAW264.7 cells," *International Journal of Biological Macromolecules*, Volume 163, 2020, Pages 270-278, ISSN 0141-8130, https://doi.org/10.1016/j.ijbiomac.2020.06.269.

Yu JC, et al. "Application of dendritic cells in tumor immunotherapy and progress in the mechanism of anti-tumor effect of Astragalus polysaccharide modulating dendritic cells: a review." *Biomed Pharmacother.* 2022;155:113541.

Zao, Ruxing. "Immunometabolic Changes and Potential Biomarkers in CFS Peripheral Immune Cells Revealed by Single-Cell RNA Sequencing." *Journal of Translational Medicine*, vol. 22, no. 10, 2024, article 285, https://doi.org/10.1186/s12967-024-05710-w

Zhang, L., Koyyalamudi, S. R., Jeong, S. C., Reddy, N., Bailey, T., & Longvah, T. (2013). "Immunomodulatory activities of polysaccharides isolated from Taxillus chinensis and Uncaria rhyncophylla." *Carbohydrate Polymers*, 98(2), 1458–1465.

Text: *Jīn Guì Yào Lüè* (金匱要略)

Section: Miscellaneous Diseases (雜病篇), Discussion of Latent Heat and Recurrence

Attributed Author: Zhang Zhongjing (張仲景)

Original (related principle): "病久不愈，必有餘邪。"

Translation: "When illness does not resolve for a long time, there must be residual pathogenic Qi."

Text: *Jīn Guì Yào Lüè* (金匱要略)

Section: Miscellaneous Diseases (雜病篇)

Attributed Author: Zhang Zhongjing (張仲景)

Original: "診脈證並治，欲解內鬱，當審其脈。"

Translation: "To resolve internal constraint, one must examine the pulse carefully."

Text: *Shāng Hán Lùn* (傷寒論)

Section: Shaoyin Illness Formula Line 303: Huang Lian E Jiao Tang (黃連阿膠湯)

Attributed Author: Zhang Zhongjing (張仲景)

Original: "少陰病，得之二三日以上，心中煩，不得臥者，黃連阿膠湯主之。"

Translation: "In Shaoyin disease, if there is fever with a deep pulse, this indicates internal Heat—Huang Lian E Jiao Tang is appropriate. If the patient is restless and cannot lie down, Huang Lian E Jiao Tang governs."

Text: *Jīn Guì Yào Lüè* (金匱要略)

Section: Dysenteric Disorders (痢病篇)

Attributed Author: Zhang Zhongjing (張仲景)

Original: "有患一年數度得噤病者，至其時則發；或一年一發，發必有時。"

Translation: "Some patients suffer repeated bouts of dysentery each year, occurring at the same time; or once yearly, but always at a fixed season."

Text: *Jīn Guì Yào Lüè* (金匱要略), Chapter on Taxation Injury (勞傷篇).

Attributed Author: Zhang Zhongjing.

Original: "發汗後，身體腫，脈浮大者，桂枝加黃芪湯主之。"

Translation: "After sweating, if the body becomes swollen and the pulse is floating and large, Gui Zhi Jia Huang Qi Tang governs."

Text: *Jīn Guì Yào Lüè* (金匱要略), *Gui Zhi jia Huang Qi Tang*; *Wēn Yì Lùn* (瘟疫論), *Da Yuan Yin*

Attributed Authors: Zhang Zhongjing (張仲景, ca. 150–219 CE); Wu Youke (吳又可, 1582–1652)

Original (Gui Zhi jia Huang Qi Tang): "發汗後，身體腫，脈浮大者，桂枝加黃芪湯主之。"

Translation: "After sweating, if the body becomes swollen and the pulse is floating and large, Gui Zhi jia Huang Qi Tang governs."Original (Da Yuan Yin): "邪在膜原，氣口脈浮大者，可用大元飲宣解膜邪。" Translation: "When the pathogen resides in the membrane source and the pulse is floating and large at the Qi opening, Da Yuan Yin can be used to disperse and resolve membrane-bound pathogens."

Zhang, Y., Li, S., Wang, X., Zhang, L., Cheung, P. C. K., & Ooi, V. E. C. (2002). "Regulation on maturation and function of dendritic cells by Ganoderma lucidum polysaccharides." *Immunology Letters*, 83(3), 163–169.

Text: *Dàn Xī Xīn Fǎ* (丹溪心法)

Section: Discussion of Heat and Yin Depletion

Attributed Author: Zhu Danxi (朱丹溪, 1281–1358)

Original: "熱伏下焦，耗人津液。"

Translation: "Heat conceals itself in the lower burner and consumes the body's fluids."

Text: *Dàn Xī Xīn Fǎ* (丹溪心法)

Section: On the Eight Depressions (八鬱篇)

Attributed Author: Zhu Danxi (朱丹溪, 1281–1358); elaborated by Ye Tianshi (葉天士) and others

Original: "鬱有八端：氣、血、濕、痰、食、火、暑、驚。"

Translation: "There are eight forms of constraint: Qi, Blood, Dampness, Phlegm, Food, Fire, Summer-Heat, and Fright." The bracketed depressions are those which were not considered to be the original six(or eight) but are often included by later physicians.

Zhu, N., Lv, X., Wang, Y., Li, J., Liu, Y., Lu, W., Yang, L., Zhao, J., Wang, F., & Zhang, L. W. (2016). "Comparison of immunoregulatory effects of polysaccharides from three natural herbs and cellular uptake in dendritic cells." *International Journal of Biological Macromolecules*, 93(Pt A), 940–951.

Zuo, W., He, D., Liang, C., Du, S., Hua, Z., Nie, Q., … & Zhan, Y. (2024). "The persistence of SARS-CoV-2 in tissues and its association with long COVID symptoms: A cross-sectional cohort study in China." *The Lancet Infectious Diseases*, 24(8), 845–855. https://doi.org/10.1016/S1473-3099(24)00171-3